BIOLOGY
The Dynamics of Life

Concept Mapping

Glencoe
McGraw-Hill

New York, New York   Columbus, Ohio   Woodland Hills, California   Peoria, Illinois

A GLENCOE PROGRAM
BIOLOGY: THE DYNAMICS OF LIFE

Student Edition
Teacher Wraparound Edition
Laboratory Manual, SE and TE
Reinforcement and Study Guide, SE and TE
Content Mastery, SE and TE
Section Focus Transparencies and Masters
Reteaching Skills Transparencies and Masters
Basic Concepts Transparencies and Masters
BioLab and MiniLab Worksheets
Concept Mapping
Chapter Assessment
Critical Thinking/Problem Solving
Spanish Resources
Tech Prep Applications
Biology Projects

Computer Test Bank Software and Manual
   WINDOWS/MACINTOSH
Lesson Plans
Block Scheduling
Inside Story Poster Package
English/Spanish Audiocassettes
MindJogger Videoquizzes
Interactive CD-ROM
Videodisc Program
Glencoe Science Professional Series:
   Exploring Environmental Issues
   Performance Assessment in the Biology Classroom
   Alternate Assessment in the Science Classroom
   Cooperative Learning in the Science Classroom
   Using the Internet in the Science Classroom

Send all inquiries to:
Glencoe/McGraw-Hill
936 Eastwind Drive
Westerville, OH 43081

ISBN 0-02-828253-1
Printed in the United States of America.
1 2 3 4 5 6 7 8 9 10   047   08 07 06 05 04 03 02 01 00 99

Contents

These *Concept Mapping* worksheets reinforce and extend the graphic organizational skills introduced in the Skill Handbook of the Student Edition of **Biology: The Dynamics of Life**. Concept maps are visual representations of relationships among particular concepts. By using these worksheets, students will gain experience with three different types of concept mapping: the *network tree*, which shows causal information, group hierarchies, and branching procedures; the *events chain*, which describes the stages of a process, the steps in a linear procedure, or a sequence of events; and the *cycle map*, which shows how a series of events interacts to produce a set of results again and again.

There is one *Concept Mapping* worksheet for each chapter in the Student Edition. Each worksheet is keyed to a specific section or sections in the chapter so that you can assign the sheet at the most relevant time. An entire section may be mapped or just a few key concepts from that section. Answers to all *Concept Mapping* worksheets are provided on reduced pages at the back of the book.

Chapter 1 Biology: The Study of Life

Use with Chapter 1, Section 1.1

Characteristics of Living Things

Complete the concept map on the characteristics of living things. Use these words or phrases once: *particular functions, grow, stimuli, specialized parts, environment, species, new structures, produce fertile offspring, adjust, continuation, similar organisms, living matter, interbreed, organization, reproduce.*

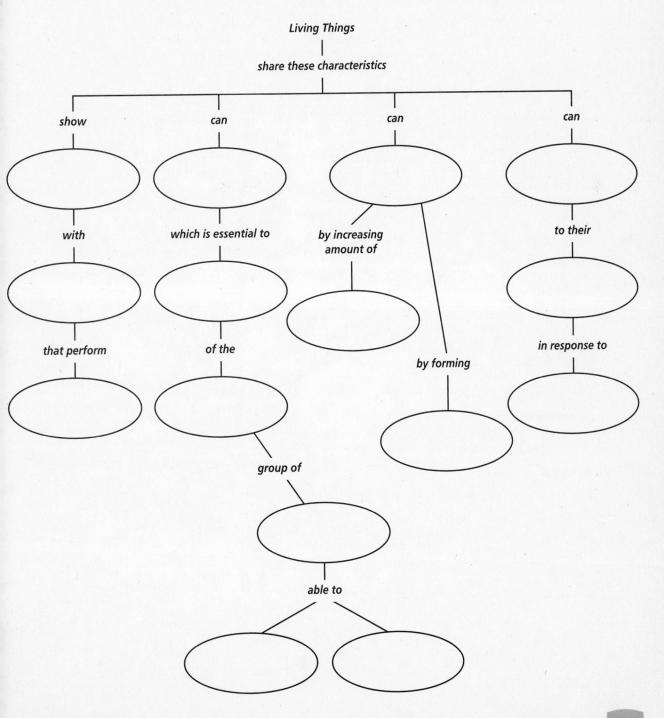

Chapter
2   Principles of Ecology

Use with Chapter 2, Section 2.2

Food Needs in a Community

Complete the concept map on food needs in a community. Use these words or phrases once: *heterotrophs, decomposers, do not make own food, absorb nutrients from dead organisms, eat autotrophs, eat other heterotrophs, herbivores, photosynthesis, autotrophs, carnivores.*

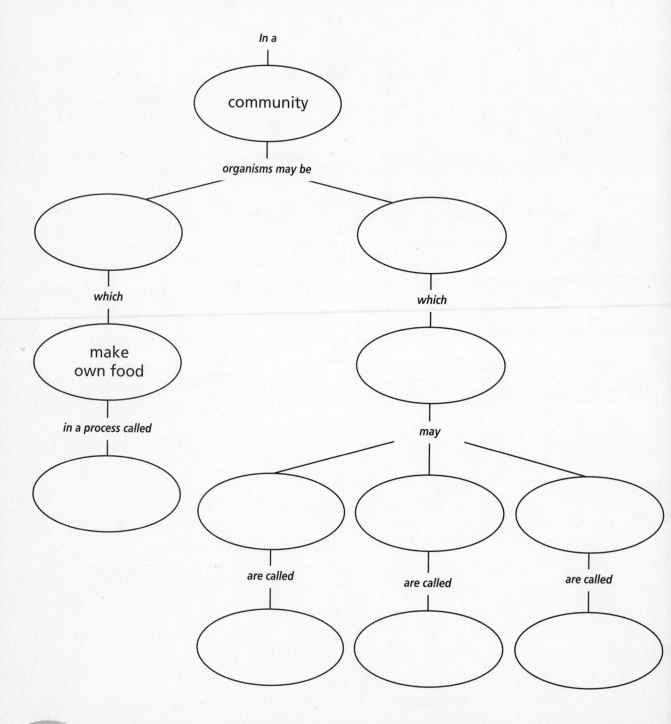

Chapter 3   Communities and Biomes

Use with Chapter 3, Section 3.1

Natural Changes in Communities

Complete the concept map on natural changes in communities. Use these words or phrases one or more times: *colonization of new sites, primary succession, pioneer species, climax community, succession, soil, disruption, natural disaster, human action, secondary succession, larger plants, rocks.*

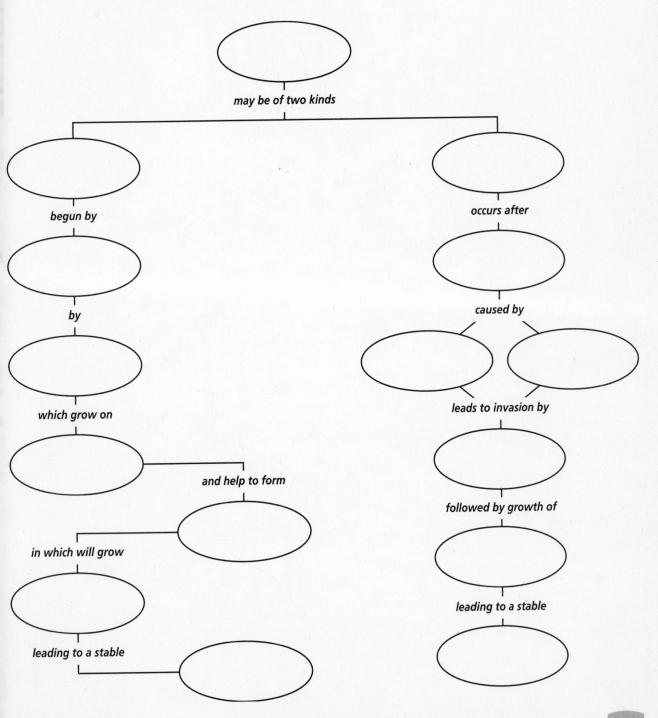

Chapter 4 Population Biology

Use with Chapter 4, Section 4.1

Population Control

Complete the concept map on factors that control the sizes of populations. Use these words or phrases once: *temperature, competition, density-dependent, disease, food supply, limiting factors, more intense as population increases, habitat disruption, parasitism, predation, same regardless of population size.*

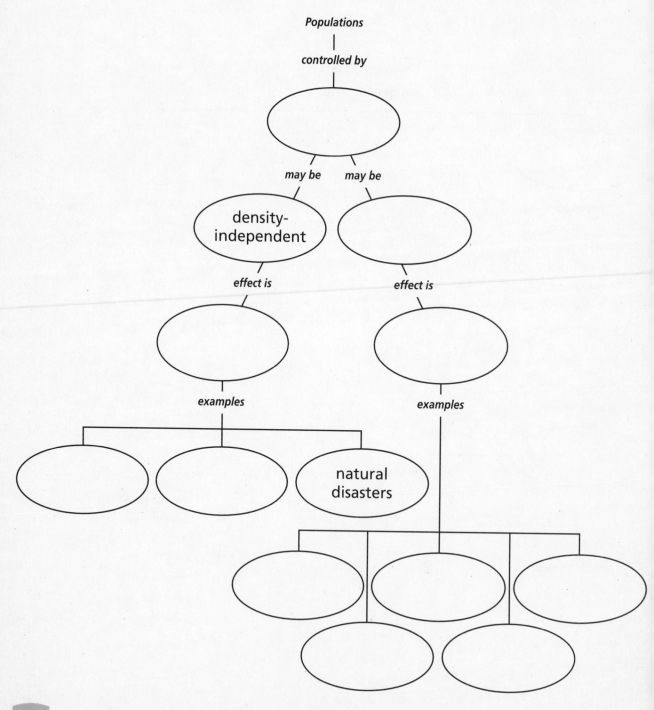

Chapter 5 Biological Diversity and Conservation

Biological Diversity

Complete the concept map on biological diversity. Use these words or phrases once: *pollution, nature, large predators, trash, variety of foods, native species, habitat degradation, people, chemicals in runoff, medicines, food webs, introduction of exotic species, habitat fragmentation, migratory organisms, acid precipitation, stability of ecosystems.*

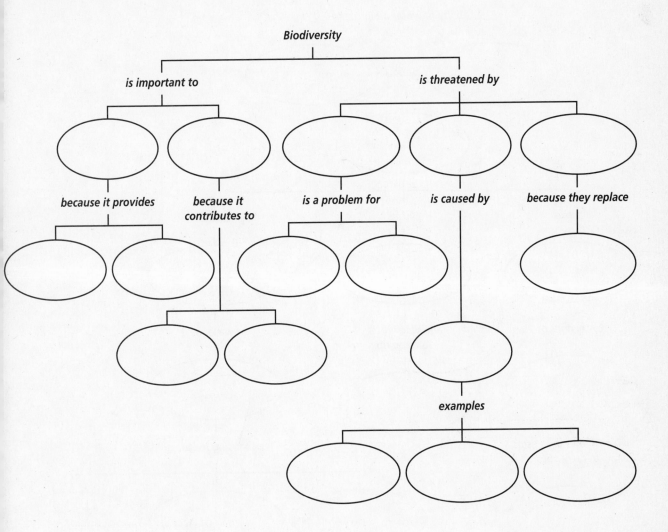

Chapter 6 The Chemistry of Life

Properties of Water Important to Living Systems

Complete the concept map on the properties of water. Use these words or phrases once: *other water molecules, float in water, hydrogen bond with, resistance, thin plant tubes, temperature, be less dense, capillary action, expansion, attract, break rocks into soil, freezes, cellular functions.*

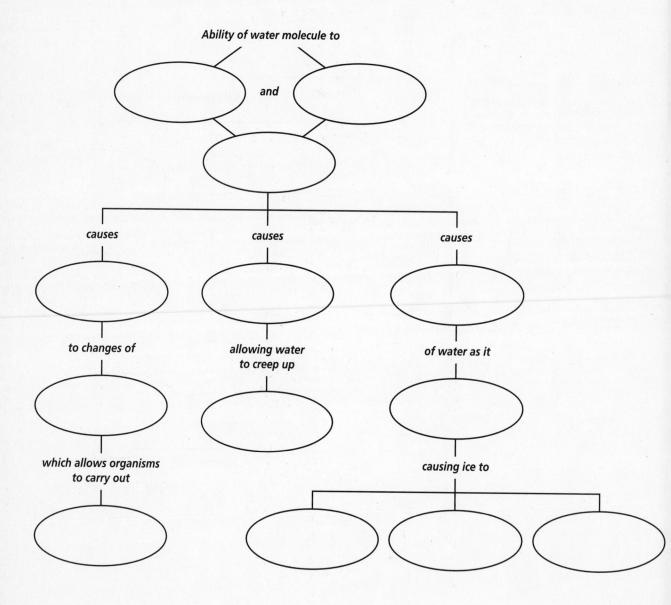

Chapter

7 A View of the Cell

Concept Mapping

Use with Chapter 7, Section 7.3

Recycling in the Cell

Complete the concept map on recycling in a cell. Use these words or phrases one or more times: *lysosomes, food particles, a membrane, bacteria and viruses, cell proteins, tail, vacuoles, worn-out cell parts, digesting it, digestive enzymes.*

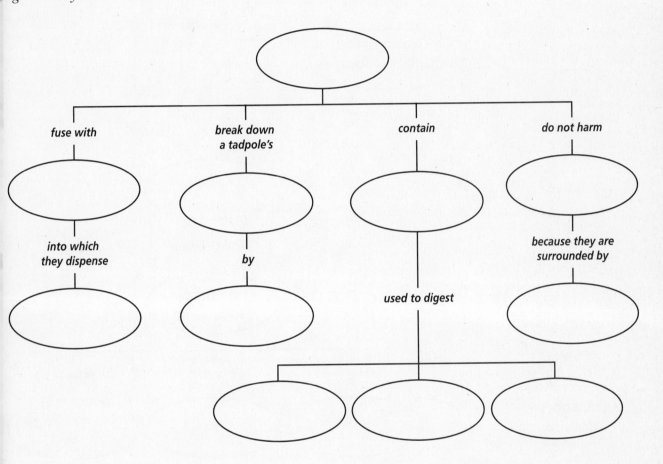

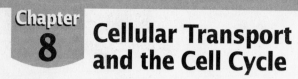

Chapter 8 Cellular Transport and the Cell Cycle

Transport Through Membranes

Complete the concept map on transport of materials through membranes. Use these words or phrases one or more times: *simple diffusion, energy, higher concentration, lower concentration, osmosis, passive, facilitated diffusion.*

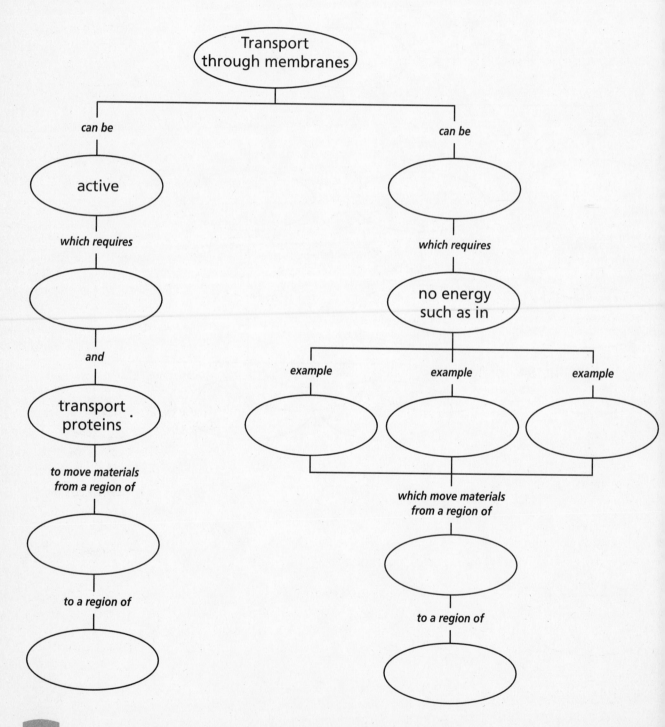

Chapter 9 Energy in a Cell

Photosynthesis: Trapping Energy

Complete the concept map describing photosynthesis. Use these words or phrases once: *chemical energy, oxygen, light-dependent reactions, chlorophyll, stroma, glucose, water, sunlight, oxygen, carbon dioxide, hydrogen ions, chloroplasts.*

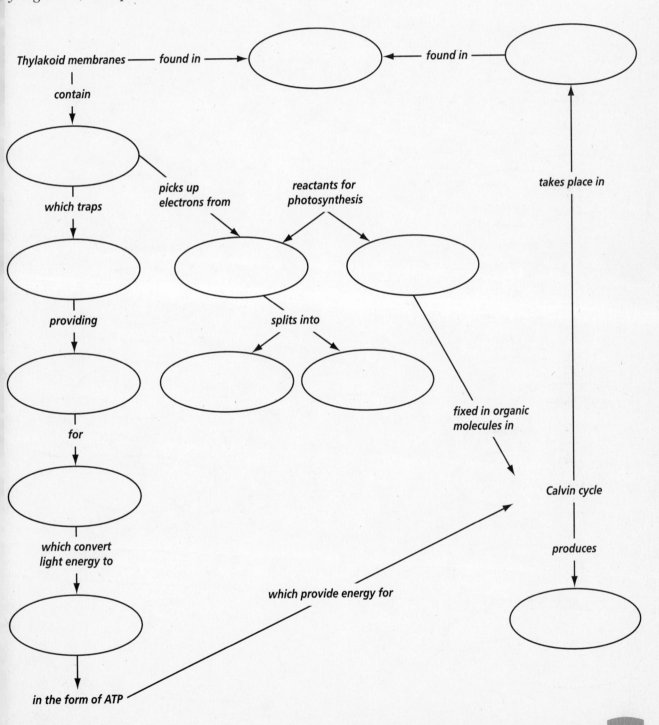

Chapter 10 Mendel and Meiosis

Concept Mapping

Use with Chapter 10, Section 10.2

Mitosis/Meiosis

Complete the concept map comparing mitosis and meiosis. Use these words or phrases one or more times: *diploid cell, one cell division, four haploid cells, original cell, two cell divisions, body cell, same, chromosomes, gamete-producing cell, half, two diploid cells.*

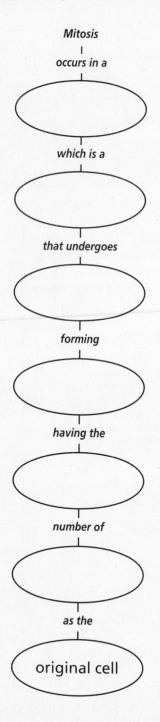

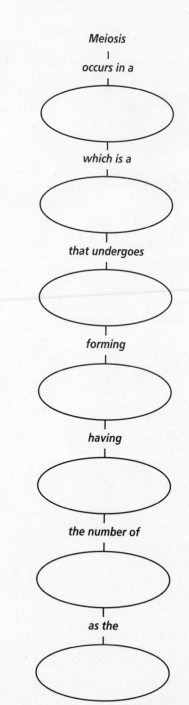

Chapter
11 DNA and Genes

DNA and RNA

Complete the concept map to show how DNA and RNA are alike and how they are different. Use these words or phrases once: *ACGT, ACGU, DNA, deoxyribose, double chain, mRNA, ribose, yes, no, nucleus, nucleus and cytoplasm, RNA, rRNA, tRNA.*

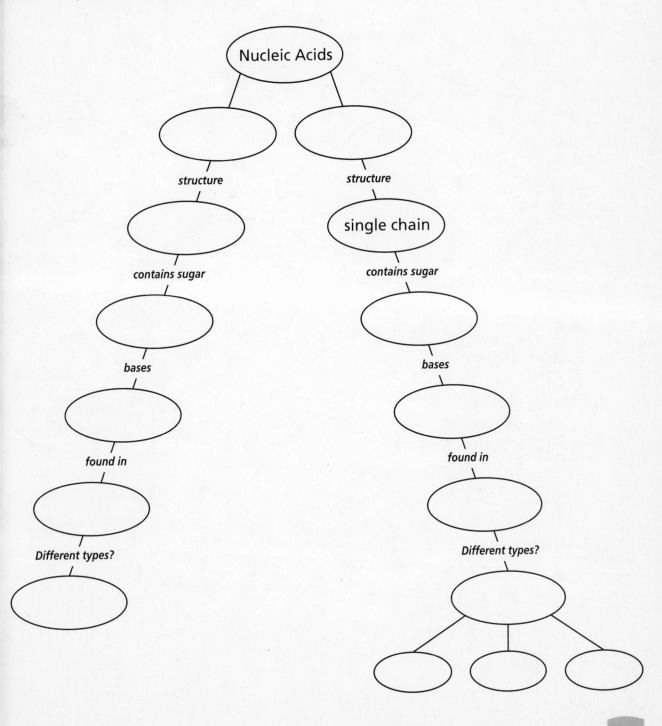

Chapter 12 Patterns of Heredity and Human Genetics

Use with Chapter 12, Section 12.1

Human Autosomal Genetic Disorders

Complete the concept map on human autosomal genetic disorders. Use these words or phrases one or more times: *Tay-Sachs disease, recessive allele, phenylketonuria, dominant allele, lungs and pancreas, central nervous system, cystic fibrosis.*

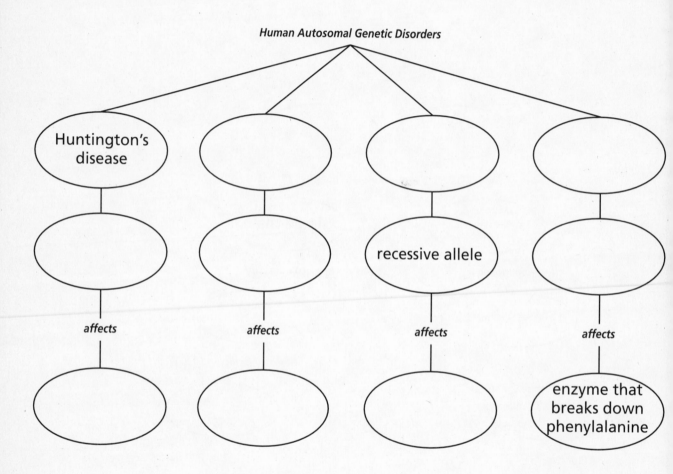

Chapter
13 Genetic Technology

The Human Genome Project

Complete the concept map on the human genome project. Use these words or phrases one or more times: *chromosomes, frequency of crossovers, distance between genes, polymerase chain reaction, meiosis, the 80 000 genes, DNA fragments of sperm cells, the 46 human chromosomes.*

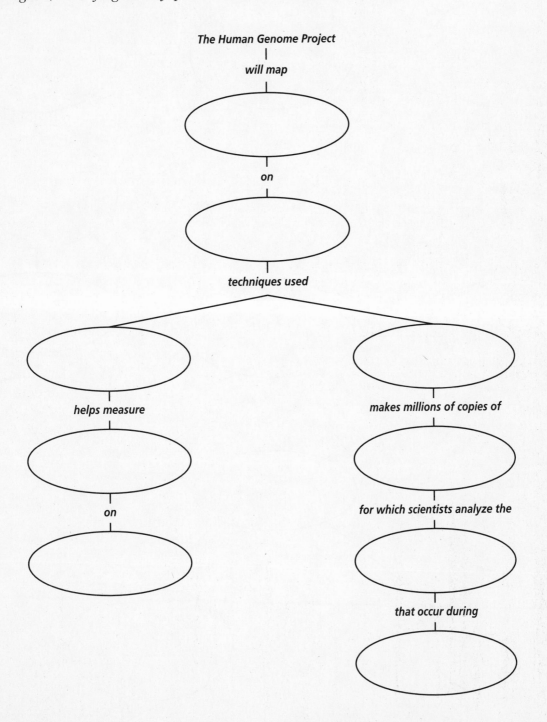

Formation of a Fossil

Make an events chain to show how fossils found in sedimentary rocks are formed, discovered, and dated.

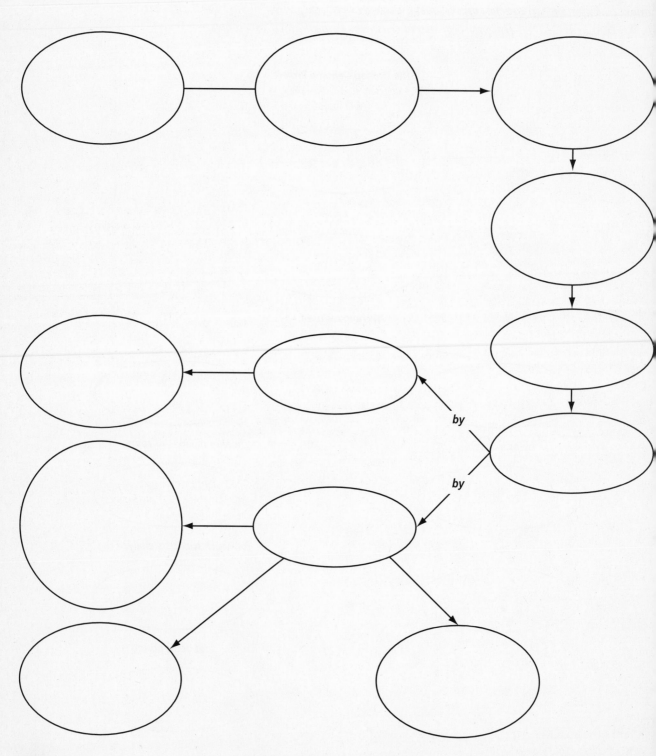

Chapter
15 The Theory of Evolution

Use with Chapter 15, Section 15.1

Evidence of Evolution

Complete the concept map on evidence of evolution. Use these words or phrases once: *anatomy, embryology, homologous parts, nucleotide sequences, vestigial organs.*

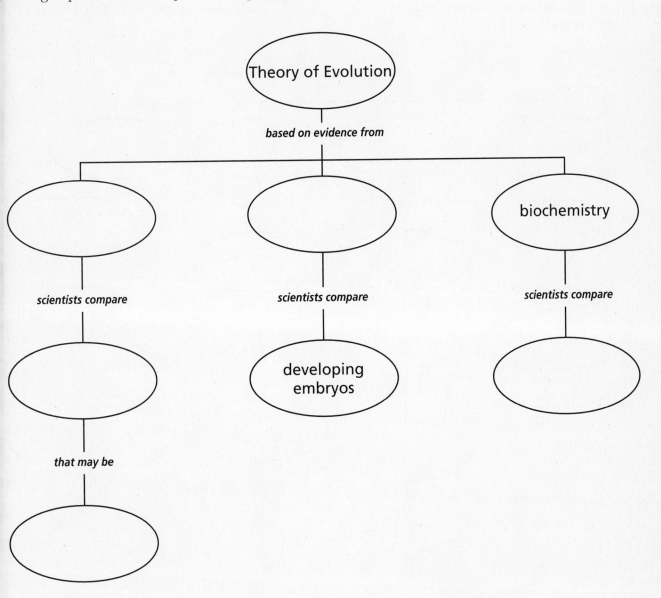

Characteristics of Primates

Complete the concept map on the characteristics of primates. Use each of these words or phrases once: *grasping and clinging, memory, flexible joints, perception, mobility, face forward, large brain, hip, hands, distance, ball-and-socket structure, complex mental functions, opposable thumb, depth, use of tools, binocular vision, shoulder, eating.*

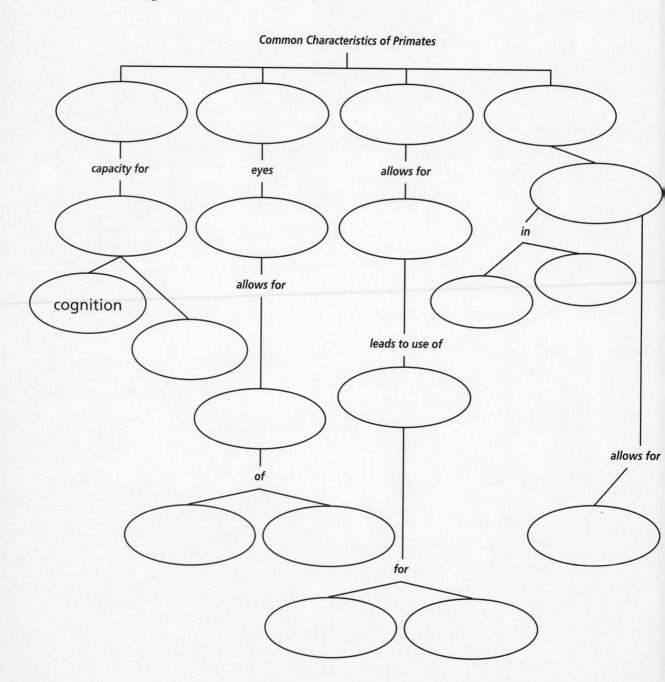

Chapter 17 Organizing Life's Diversity

Classifying Organisms

Make a concept map identifying the six kingdoms into which organisms are classified. Show whether the organisms in each kingdom are prokaryotes or eukaryotes; unicellular or multicellular; autotrophs or heterotrophs.

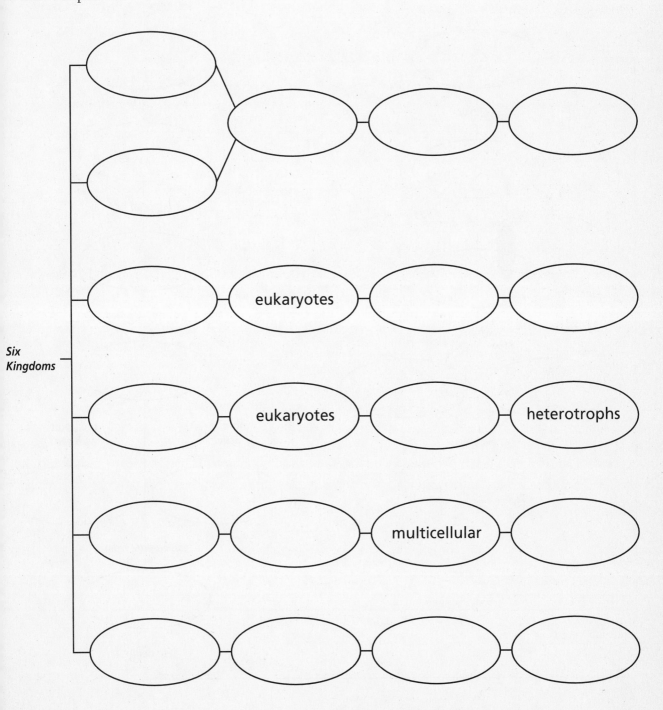

Six Kingdoms

eukaryotes

eukaryotes heterotrophs

multicellular

Viral Reproductive Cycles

Complete the chains of events for the lytic cycle and the lysogenic cycle. Use these words or phrases one or more times: *lytic cycle, host cell, copies viral genes, kills host cell, lysogenic cycle, host cell's chromosome, a provirus, alters, continue, viral DNA, replication of host cell, makes viral protein coat.*

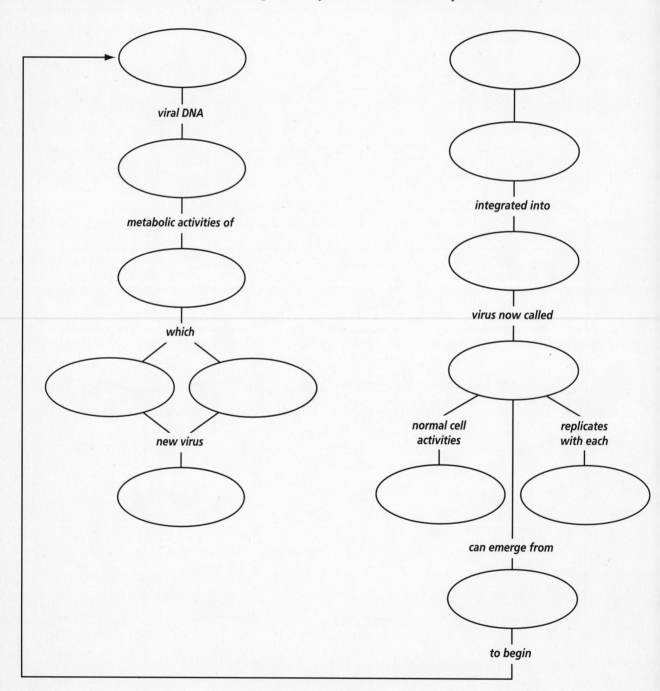

Chapter 19 Protists

Slime Molds

Make a concept map comparing the life cycle of a plasmodial slime mold with that of a cellular slime mold. Use these words or phrases once: *meiosis, individual haploid cells that divide by mitosis, haploid during entire life cycle, no meiosis, Acrasiomycota, Myxomycota, cytoplasm with diploid nuclei but no cell walls or membranes, cells become a multicellular mass of amoeboid cells, haploid spores form gametes, engulfs organisms, transforms into many separate spore-producing structures.*

Life Cycles of Slime Molds

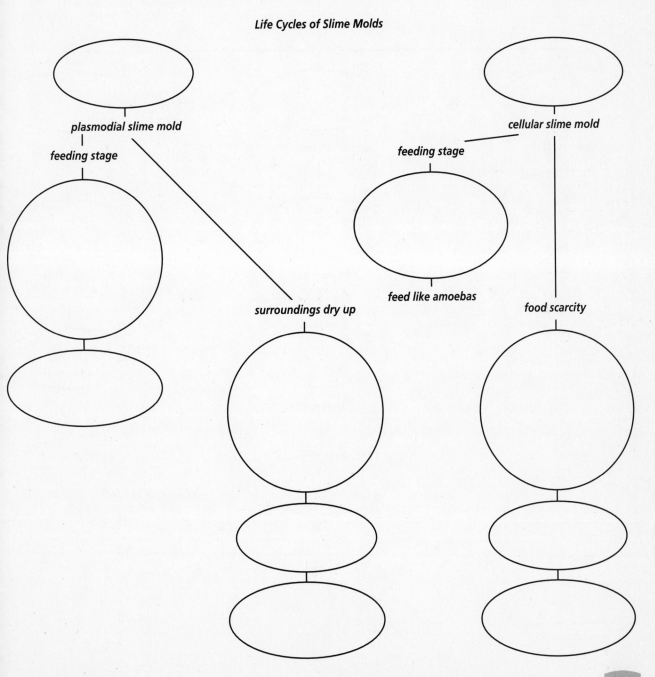

Chapter 20 Fungi

Feeding Relationships of Fungi

Complete the concept map on the feeding relationships of fungi. Use these words or phrases once: *decomposers, mutualists, organic substances, living hosts, symbiotically, waste matter, raw materials, parasites, the host's cells, living organisms, other organisms, dead organisms, haustoria.*

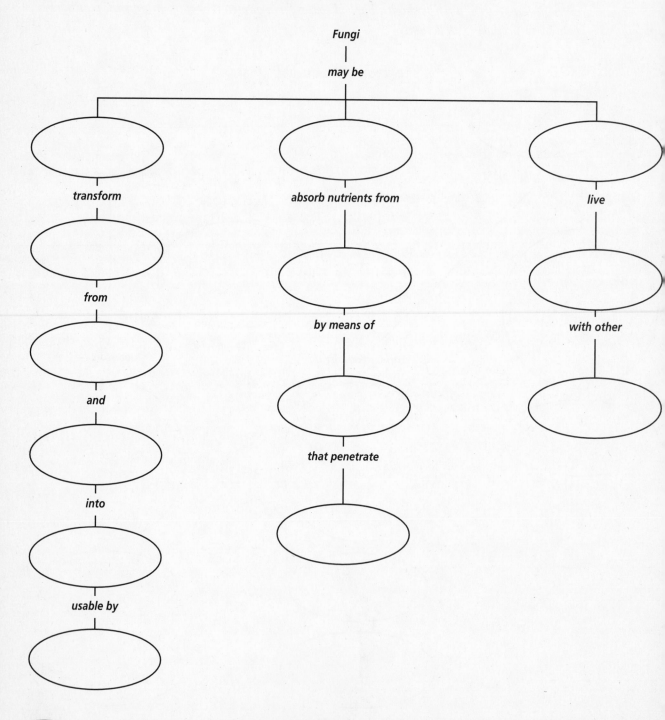

Fungi

may be

transform	absorb nutrients from	live
from	by means of	with other
and	that penetrate	
into		
usable by		

Chapter
21 What Is a Plant?

Use with Chapter 21, Section 21.1

Adaptations of Land plants

Make a concept map on the adaptations that land plants have for living on land. Include structure and function in the map. Use these words or phrases once: *root, cuticle, stem, seed, leaf.*

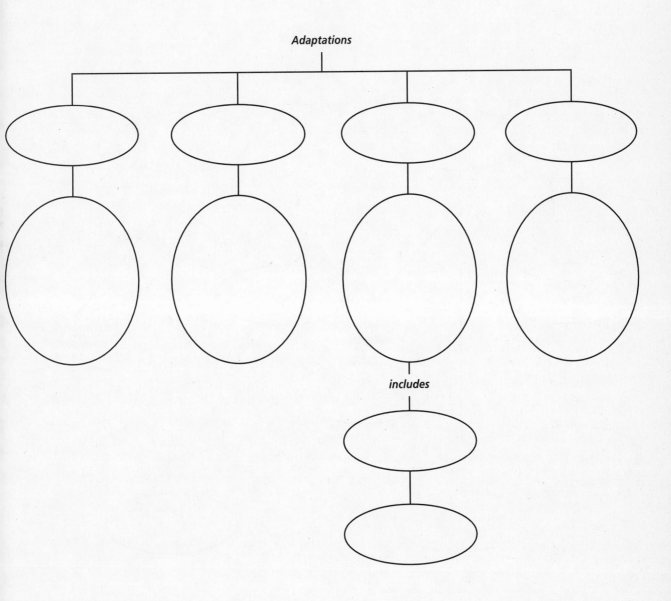

22 The Diversity of Plants

Characteristics of Anthophyta

Complete this concept map comparing the characteristics of the two classes of anthophyta. Use these words or phrases once: *monocotyledons, one seed leaf, two seed leaves, dicotyledons, three, parallel veins, four or five, branched veins.*

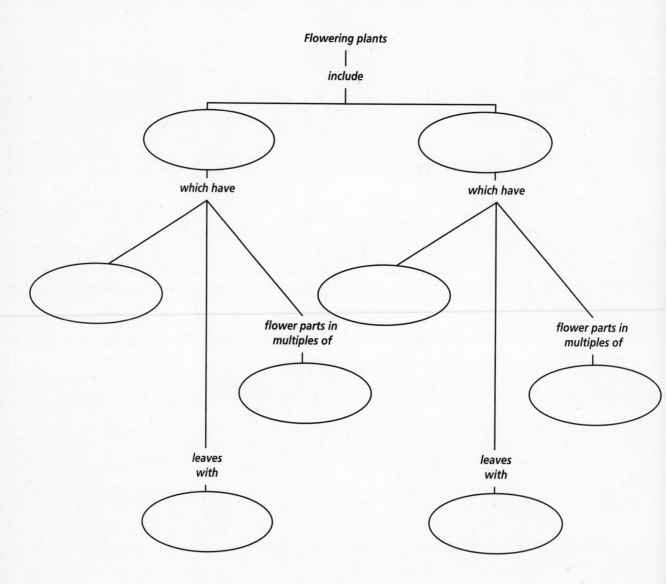

Chapter
23 **Plant Structure and Function**   *Use with Chapter 23, Section 23.1*

Concept Mapping

Plant Tissues

Complete the concept map of plant tissues. Use these words or phrases once: *apical meristem, cork cambium, dermal, ground, guard cell, lateral meristem, phloem, stomata, vascular, vascular cambium, xylem.*

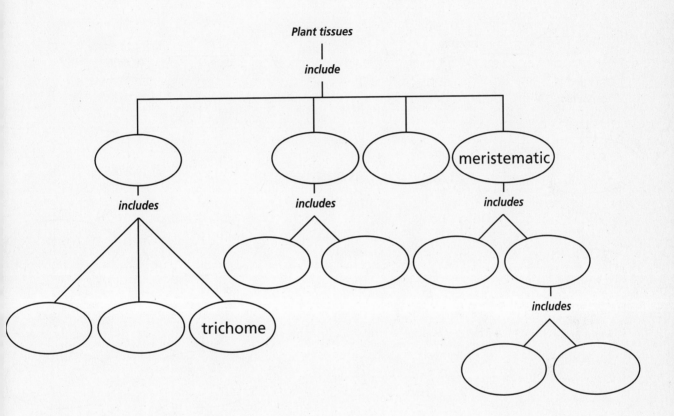

Chapter

24 Reproduction in Plants

Life Cycle of a Fern

Complete the concept map for the life cycle of a fern. Use these words or phrases once: *gametophyte (prothallus), sperm, haploid spores, fronds, antheridia, diploid zygote, eggs, sporangia, archegonia, sori, sporophyte, fertilized egg, rhizome.*

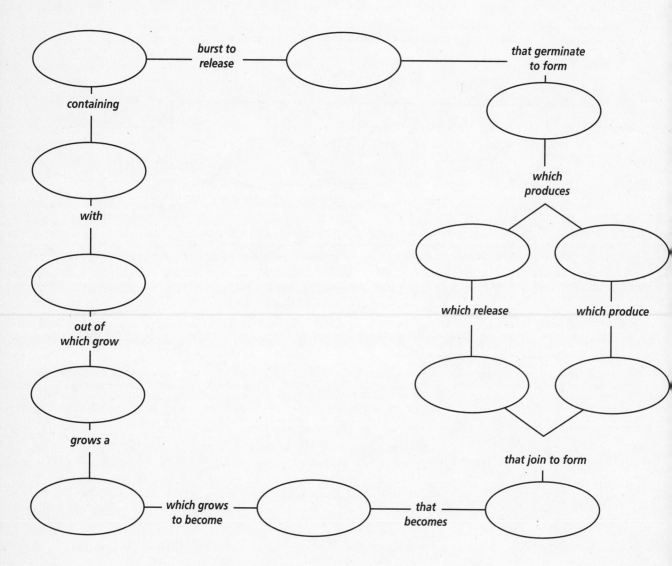

Chapter
25   **What Is an Animal?**

Body Structure of Animals with Bilateral Symmetry

Complete the network tree concept map for the body structure of animals with bilateral symmetry. Use these words or phrases one or more times: *acoelomate animals; no body cavity; support; roundworms; humans, insects, and fishes; mesoderm; complex internal organs; fluid-filled body cavity; coelomate animals, flatworms; muscles.*

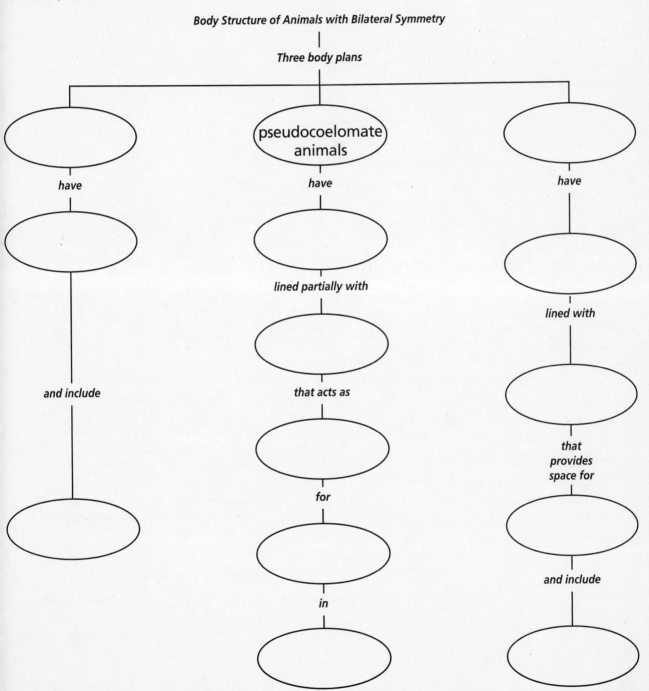

Sponges

Complete this concept map showing structure and function in a sponge. Use these words or phrases once: *collar cells; no tissues, organs, or organ systems; amoebocytes; pore cells; two cell layers; filter feeding; eukaryotic multicellular heterotrophs; epithelial cells; no body cavity; spicules.*

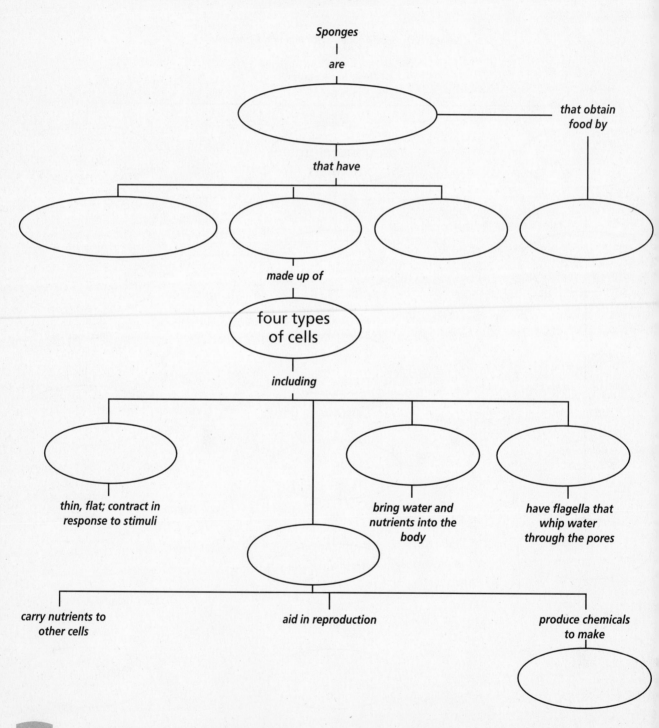

Chapter 27   Mollusks and Segmented Worms

Use with Chapter 27, Section 27.2

Segmented Worms

Complete this network tree concept map showing the body organization of the earthworm. Use these words or phrases once: *ventral nerve cord, coelom, brain, excretory organs, bilateral symmetry, crop, reproduction, gizzard, nephridia, anus, nerve fibers, blood, esophagus, segmented body, mouth, blood vessels.*

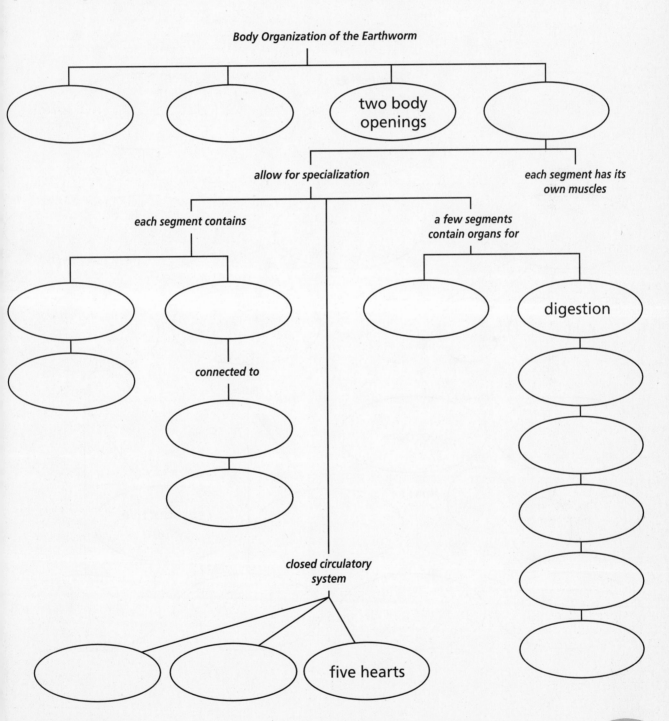

Chapter 28 **Arthropods**

Metamorphosis in Insects

Complete the concept map on metamorphosis in insects. Use these words or phrases one or more times: *complete, internal chemicals, larva, tissue reorganization, adult, four stages, nymph, incomplete, fully developed appendages, reproductive system, egg, grows, three stages, caterpillar, eats leaves, replacement of tissues, molts, pupa.*

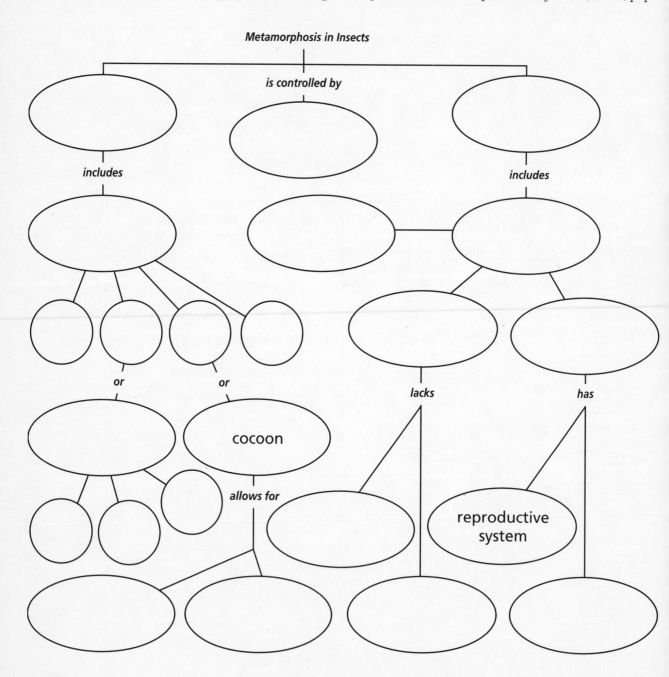

Chapter 29 Echinoderms and Invertebrate Chordates

Characteristics of Invertebrate Chordates

Complete the concept map of the characteristics of invertebrate chordates. Use these words or phrases once: *the dorsal hollow nerve cord, posterior portion, the brain, the notochord, each muscle block, the spinal cord, a pair, gill slits, muscle blocks, the tail, the pharynx, nerves, anterior portion.*

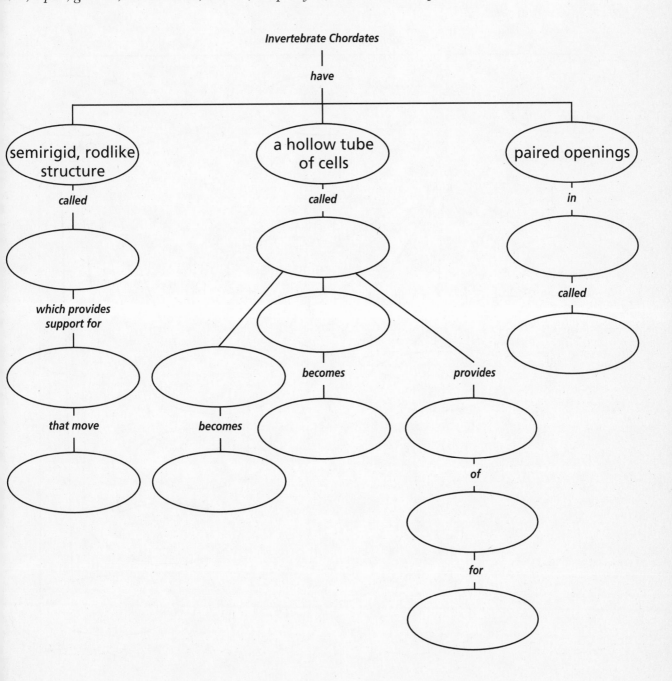

Chapter
30 Fishes and Amphibians

Phylum Chordata

Complete the concept map showing the subphyla and characteristics of the phylum Chordata. Use these words or phrases once: *Urochordata, birds, bilateral symmetry, closed circulatory system, fishes, Cephalochordata, complex brain and sense organs, amphibians, coelomate body plan, Vertebrata, reptiles, efficient respiratory system.*

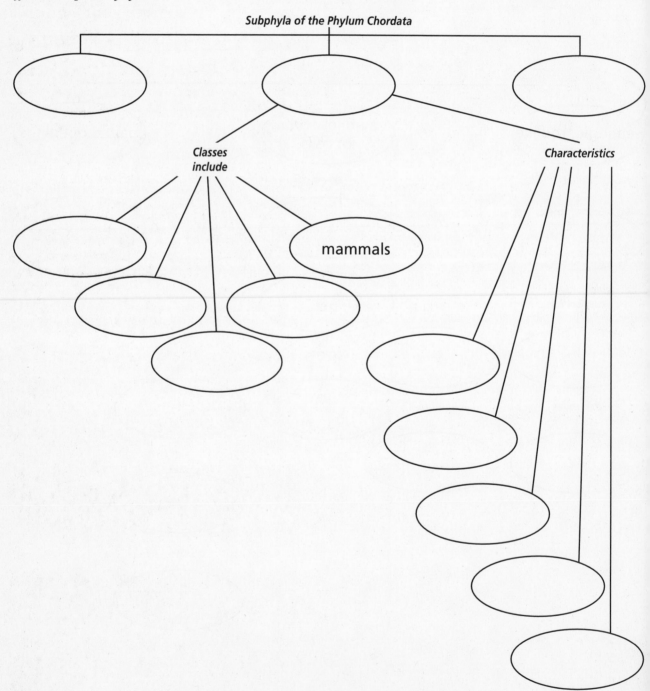

Concept Mapping

Chapter
31   Reptiles and Birds

Use with Chapter 31, Section 31.2

Adaptations for Flight

Complete the concept map of the adaptations that allow birds to fly. Use these words or phrases once: *powerful muscles, wings, hollow bones, inhaling, ability to maintain high energy level, lightweight body, air sacs, sternum, digestive system that can handle large amounts of food, exhaling, beak made of keratin, feathers, no teeth or jaw, lungs, oxygenated air.*

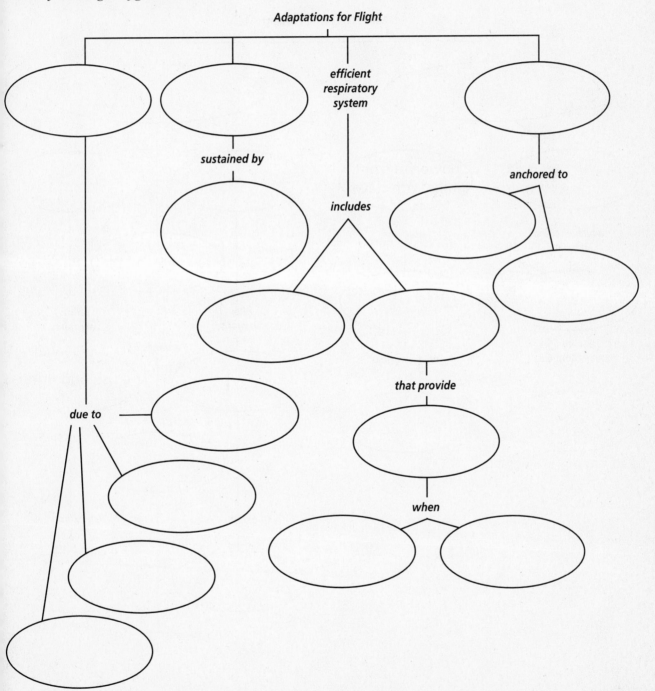

Mammalian Adaptations for Feeding

Complete the concept map of mammalian adaptations for obtaining and consuming food. Use these words or phrases once: *grasp, beavers, premolars and molars, digging, limbs for gathering food, puncture and tear, opposable thumb, gnaw, moles, canines, primates, tigers, horses, teeth for eating food, incisors.*

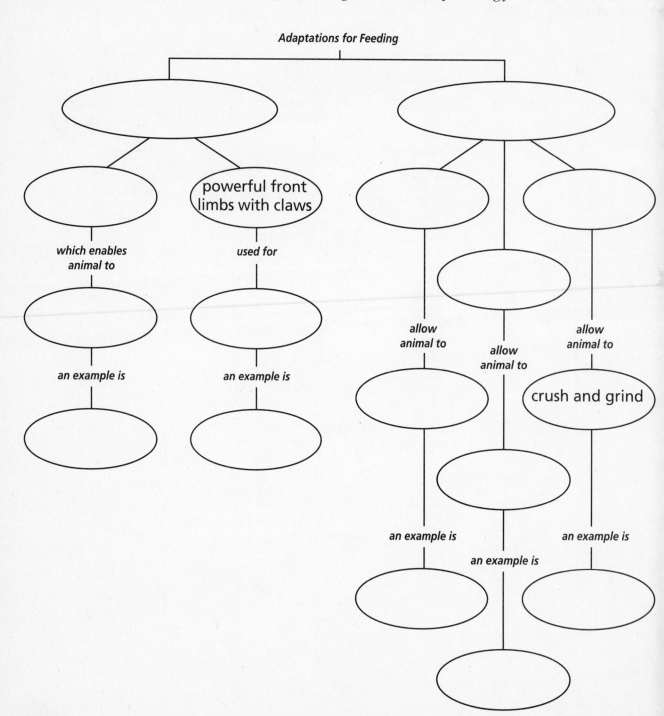

Chapter 33 **Animal Behavior**

Territoriality

omplete the concept map of the role played by territoriality in the survival of species. Use these words
phrases once: *dominance hierarchy, population growth, survival, injury to either male, other animals,
gressive behavior, species as a whole, limited resources, dominance, submission of the weaker male, young,
eromones, territories.*

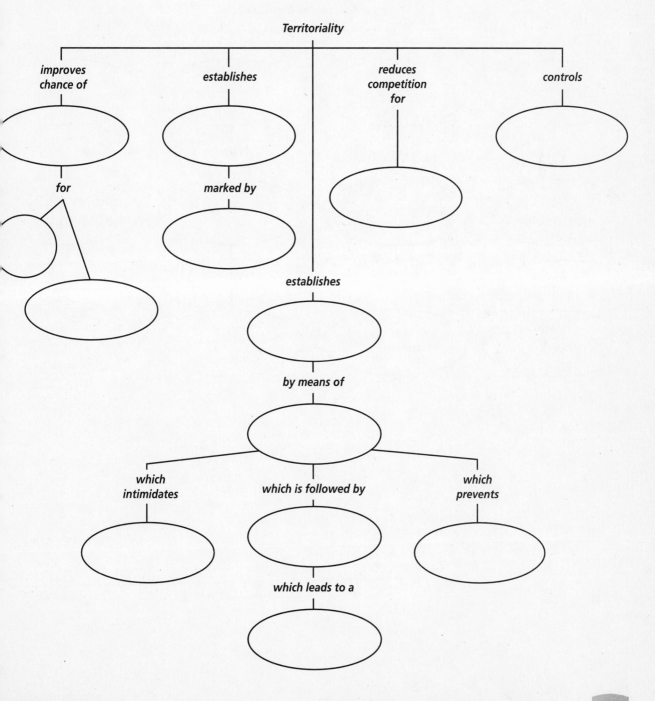

Chapter 34 Protection, Support, and Locomotion

Joints in the Human Body

Complete this concept map of the types and functions of joints in the human body. Then give examples of each type. Use these words or phrases once: *wrist, ball-and-socket, fingers, toes, rotational motion, hip, shoulder, back-and-forth motion, ankle, knee, hinge, gliding, elbow, pivot.*

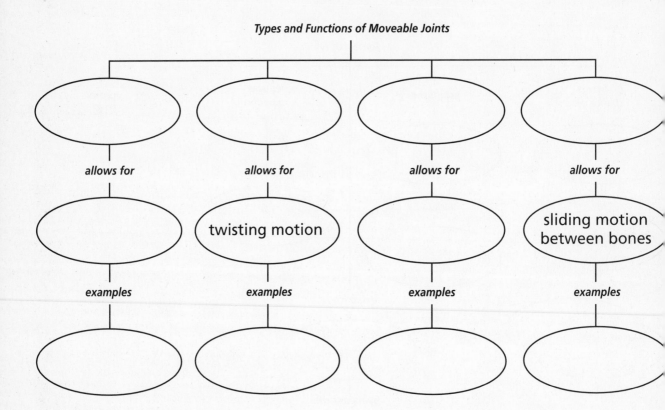

Chapter 35   The Digestive and Endocrine Systems

Carbohydrates, Fats, and Proteins in Nutrition

Complete this concept map showing the role of carbohydrates, fats, and proteins in nutrition. Use these words or phrases once: *muscles, antibodies, carbohydrates, proteins, chemicals for blood-clotting, amino acids, glycerol, body functions, fatty acids, the liver, indigestible cellulose, glycogen, fat, body cells, hormones, cell structure, enzymes, simple sugars.*

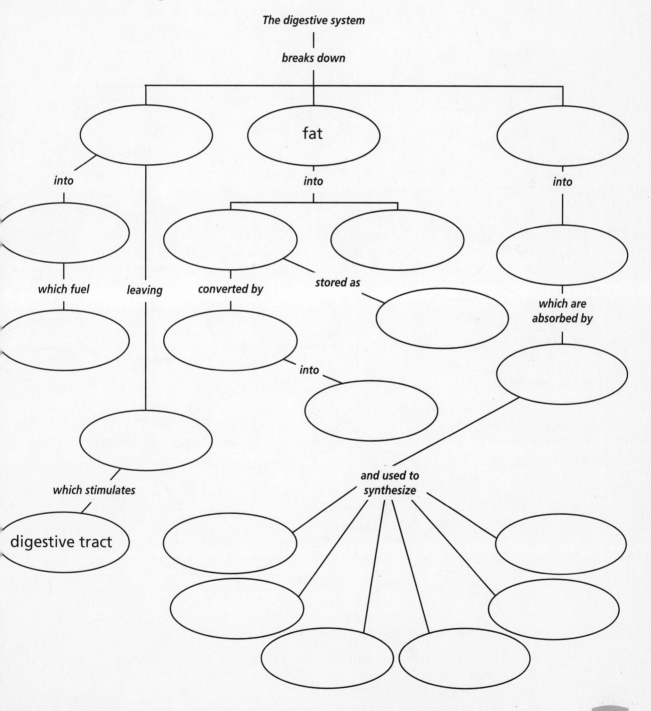

Chapter 36 **The Nervous System**

The Sense of Touch

Complete this concept map for the sense of touch. Use these words or phrases one or more times: *dermis, temperature, nerve endings, heat, cold, light pressure, eyelids, skin surface, tip of tongue, palms of hands, epidermis, fingertips, organs, muscle tissue, lower layers, heavy pressure, soles of feet.*

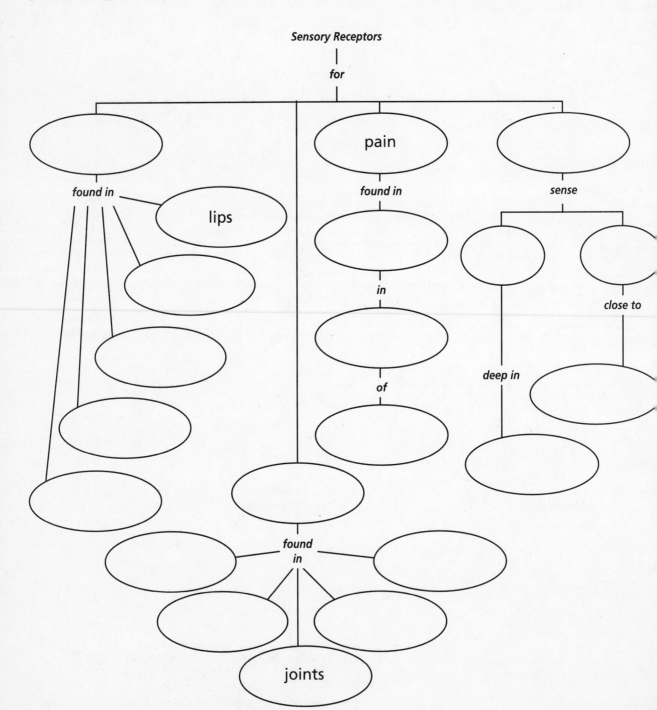

Respiration, Circulation, and Excretion

Concept Mapping

Use with Chapter 37, Section 37.2

Circulation in Humans

Complete the concept map on human circulation and heart function. Use these words or phrases once:
high O₂, low O₂, vena cava, left atrium, right ventricle, right atrium, high CO₂, low CO₂, pulmonary veins, left ventricle, aorta, lungs.

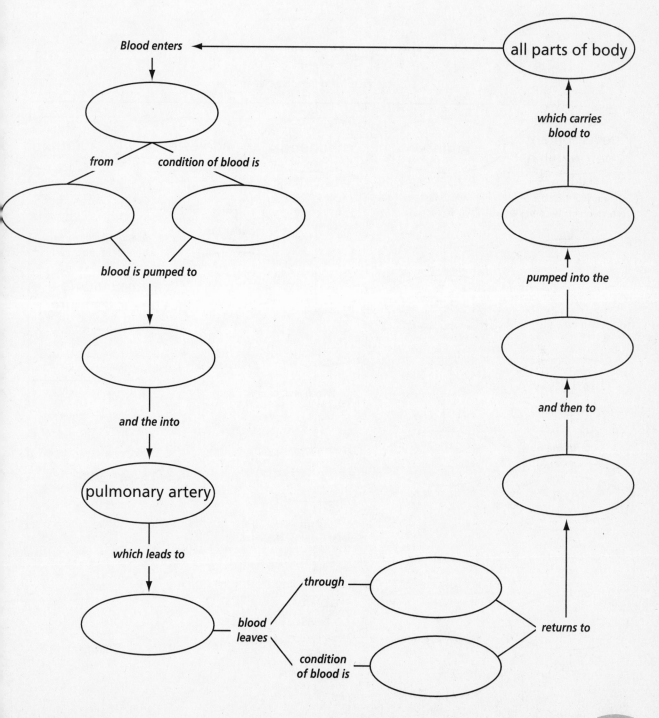

Chapter 38 Reproduction and Development

Human Growth

Make a concept map showing the different stages of human growth and their characteristics. Use these words or phrases once: *puberty, human growth, two years, embryo, zygote, fetus, slower metabolism, teen years, physical and intellectual activity.*

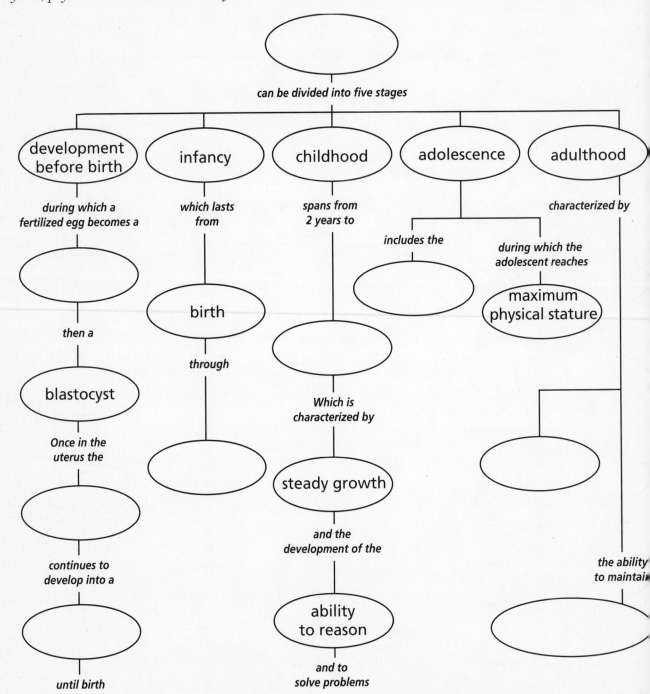

Chapter
39 Immunity from Disease

The Lymphatic System

Complete the concept map about the structure of the lymphatic system and how it defends the body against disease. Use these words or phrases one or more times: *foreign substances, two ducts, tissue fluid, lymph, white blood cells, lymph veins, protect body, nodes, bloodstream, lymphocytes, lymph capillaries.*

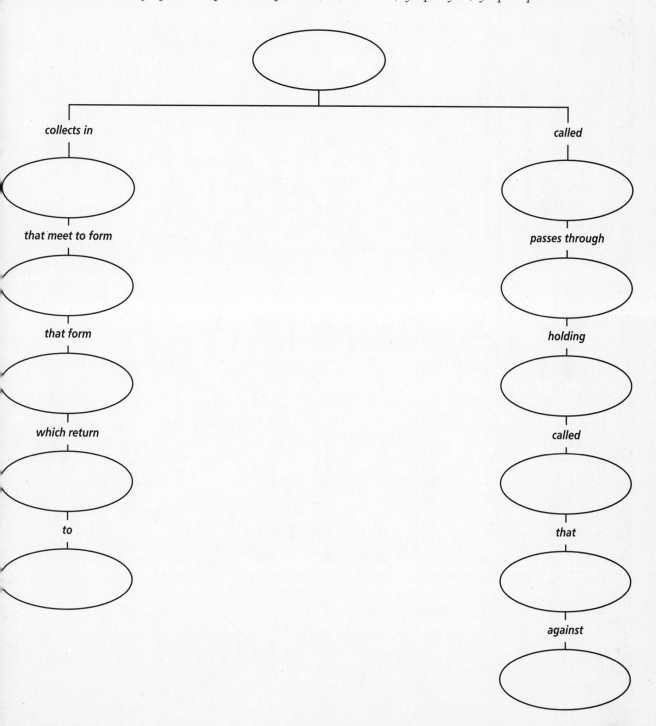

Name _____ Date _____ Class _____

Chapter 1 Biology: The Study of Life

Characteristics of Living Things

Complete the concept map on the characteristics of living things. Use these words or phrases once: *particular functions, grow, stimuli, specialized parts, environment, species, new structures, produce fertile offspring, adjust, continuation, similar organisms, living matter, interbreed, organization, reproduce.*

Living Things

share these characteristics

- **show** → **organization** → with → **specialized parts** → that perform → **particular functions**
- **can** → **reproduce** → which is essential to → **continuation** → of the → **species** → group of → **similar organisms** → able to → **produce fertile offspring** / **interbreed**
- **can** → **grow** → by increasing amount of → **living matter**; by forming → **new structures**
- **can** → **adjust** → to their → **environment** → in response to → **stimuli**

CHAPTER 1 BIOLOGY: The Dynamics of Life 1

CONCEPT MAPPING

Name _____ Date _____ Class _____

Chapter 2 Principles of Ecology

Food Needs in a Community

Complete the concept map on food needs in a community. Use these words or phrases once: *heterotrophs, decomposers, do not make own food, absorb nutrients from dead organisms, eat autotrophs, eat other heterotrophs, herbivores, photosynthesis, autotrophs, carnivores.*

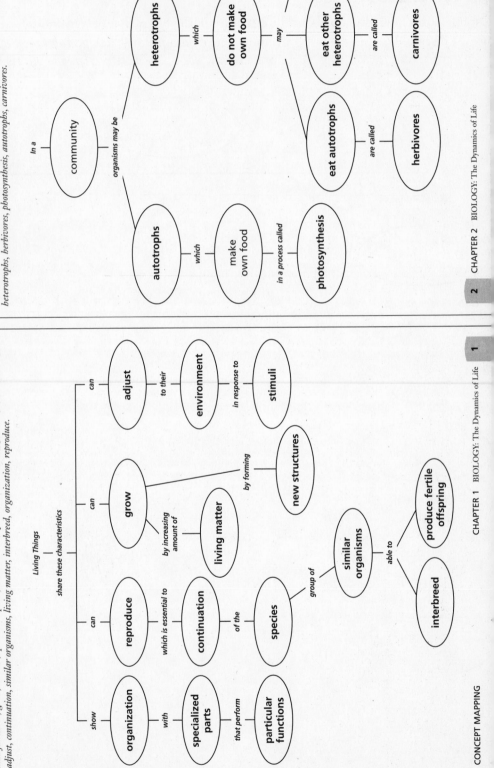

In a → **community** → organisms may be:

- **autotrophs** → which → **make own food** → in a process called → **photosynthesis**
- **heterotrophs** → which → **do not make own food** → may:
  - **eat autotrophs** → are called → **herbivores**
  - **eat other heterotrophs** → are called → **carnivores**
  - **absorb nutrients from dead organisms** → are called → **decomposers**

CHAPTER 2 BIOLOGY: The Dynamics of Life 2

CONCEPT MAPPING

Name _____ Date _____ Class _____

Concept Mapping

Chapter 3 — Communities and Biomes

Use with Chapter 3, Section 3.1

Natural Changes in Communities

Complete the concept map on natural changes in communities. Use these words or phrases one or more times: *colonization of new sites, primary succession, pioneer species, climax community, succession, soil, disruption, natural disaster, human action, secondary succession, larger plants, rocks.*

Name _____ Date _____ Class _____

Concept Mapping

Chapter 4 — Population Biology

Use with Chapter 4, Section 4.1

Population Control

Complete the concept map on factors that control the sizes of populations. Use these words or phrases once: *temperature, competition, density-dependent, disease, food supply, limiting factors, more intense as population increases, habitat disruption, parasitism, predation, same regardless of population size.*

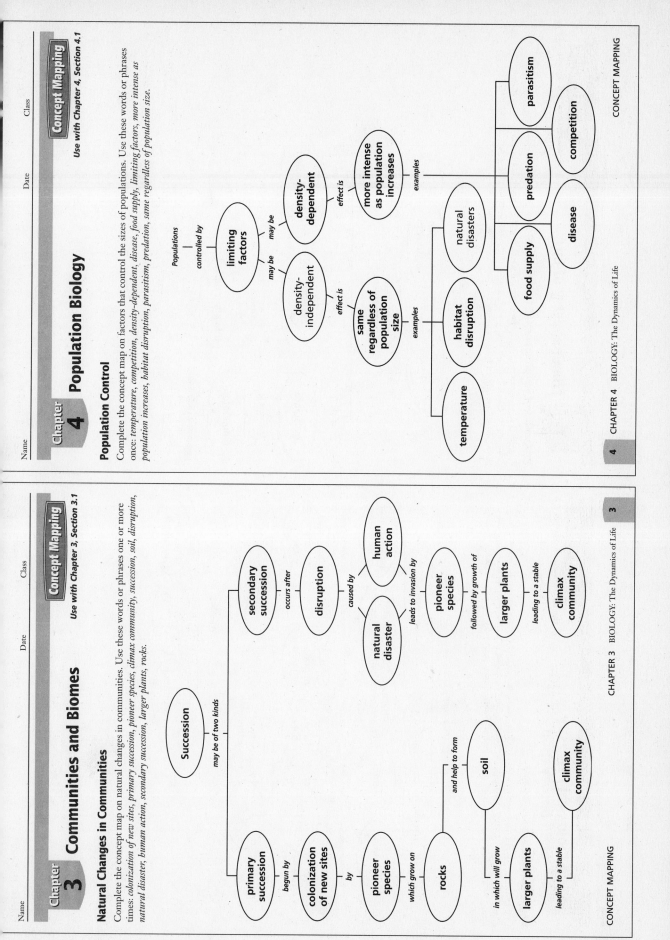

Concept Mapping

Chapter 6 — The Chemistry of Life

Use with Chapter 6, Section 6.2

Properties of Water Important to Living Systems

Complete the concept map on the properties of water. Use these words or phrases once: *other water molecules, float in water, hydrogen bond with, resistance, thin plant tubes, temperature, be less dense, capillary action, expansion, attract, break rocks into soil, freezes, cellular functions.*

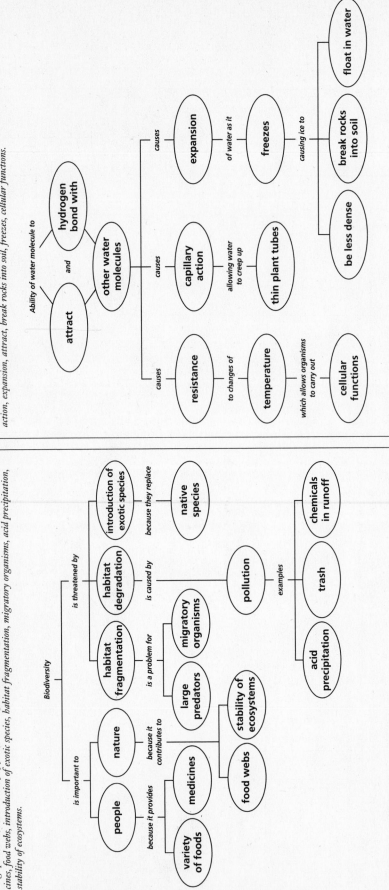

Concept Mapping

Chapter 5 — Biological Diversity and Conservation

Use with Chapter 5, Section 5.1

Biological Diversity

Complete the concept map on biological diversity. Use these words or phrases once: *pollution, nature, large predators, trash, variety of foods, native species, habitat degradation, people, chemicals in runoff, medicines, food webs, introduction of exotic species, habitat fragmentation, migratory organisms, acid precipitation, stability of ecosystems.*

Chapter 7 A View of the Cell

Recycling in the Cell

Complete the concept map on recycling in a cell. Use these words or phrases one or more times: *lysosomes, food particles, a membrane, bacteria and viruses, cell proteins, tail, vacuoles, worn-out cell parts, digesting it, digestive enzymes.*

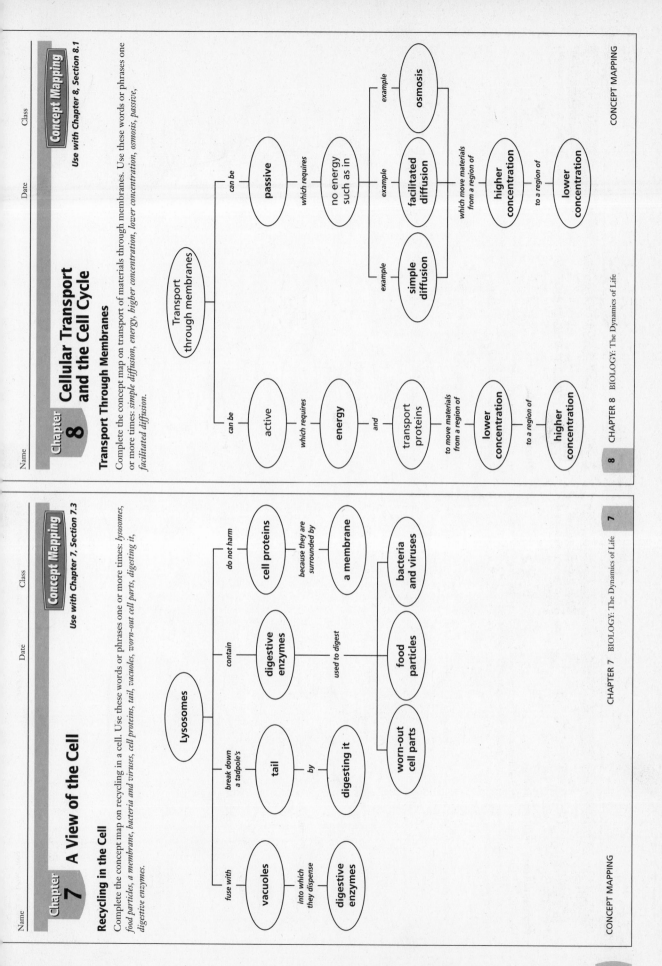

- **Lysosomes**
  - fuse with → **vacuoles** → into which they dispense → **digestive enzymes**
  - break down a tadpole's → **tail** → by → **digesting it**
    - **worn-out cell parts**
  - contain → **digestive enzymes** → used to digest → **food particles**
    - **bacteria and viruses**
  - do not harm → **cell proteins** → because they are surrounded by → **a membrane**

Chapter 8 Cellular Transport and the Cell Cycle

Transport Through Membranes

Complete the concept map on transport of materials through membranes. Use these words or phrases one or more times: *simple diffusion, energy, higher concentration, lower concentration, osmosis, passive, facilitated diffusion.*

- **Transport through membranes**
  - can be → **active** → which requires → **energy** → and → **transport proteins** → to move materials from a region of → **lower concentration** → to a region of → **higher concentration**
  - can be → **passive** → which requires → **no energy such as in**
    - example → **simple diffusion**
    - example → **facilitated diffusion**
    - example → **osmosis**
    - which move materials from a region of → **higher concentration** → to a region of → **lower concentration**

Concept Mapping

Use with Chapter 10, Section 10.2

Chapter 10   Mendel and Meiosis

Mitosis/Meiosis

Complete the concept map comparing mitosis and meiosis. Use these words or phrases one or more times: *diploid cell, one cell division, four haploid cells, original cell, two cell divisions, body cell, same, chromosomes, gamete-producing cell, half, two diploid cells.*

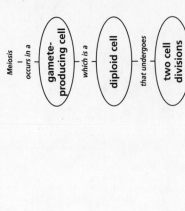

Meiosis
occurs in a
→ **gamete-producing cell**
which is a → **diploid cell**
that undergoes → **two cell divisions**
forming → **four haploid cells**
having → **half**
the number of → **chromosomes**
as the → **original cell**

Mitosis
occurs in a
→ **body cell**
which is a → **diploid cell**
that undergoes → **one cell division**
forming → **two diploid cells**
having the → **same**
number of → **chromosomes**
as the → **original cell**

Concept Mapping

Use with Chapter 9, Section 9.2

Chapter 9   Energy in a Cell

Photosynthesis: Trapping Energy

Complete the concept map describing photosynthesis. Use these words or phrases once: *chemical energy, oxygen, light-dependent reactions, chlorophyll, stroma, glucose, water, sunlight, oxygen, carbon dioxide, hydrogen ions, chloroplasts.*

Thylakoid membranes — *found in* → **chloroplasts**
found in → **stroma**
stroma ← *takes place in* — **Calvin cycle**
Calvin cycle *produces* → **glucose**

contain → **chlorophyll**
which traps → **sunlight**
providing → **energy**
for → **light-dependent reactions**
which convert light energy to → **chemical energy**
in the form of ATP
which provide energy for → **Calvin cycle**

chlorophyll *picks up electrons from* → **water**
water *reactants for photosynthesis* → **carbon dioxide**
carbon dioxide *fixed in organic molecules in* → **Calvin cycle**
water *splits into* → **hydrogen ions**
water *splits into* → **oxygen**

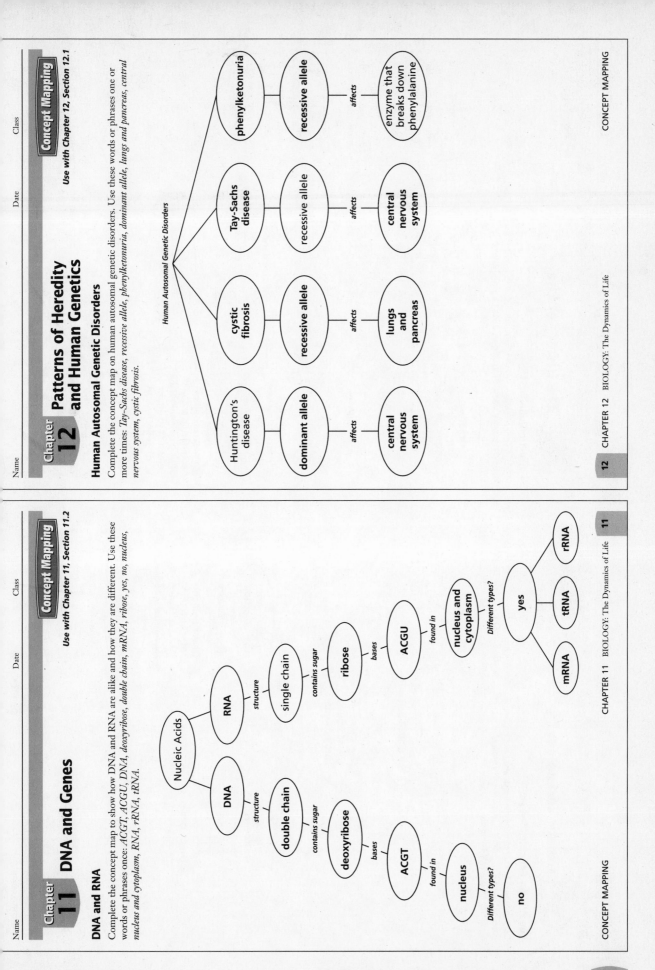

Chapter 11 DNA and Genes

DNA and RNA

Complete the concept map to show how DNA and RNA are alike and how they are different. Use these words or phrases once: *ACGT, ACGU, DNA, deoxyribose, double chain, mRNA, ribose, yes, no, nucleus, nucleus and cytoplasm, RNA, rRNA, tRNA.*

Chapter 12 Patterns of Heredity and Human Genetics

Human Autosomal Genetic Disorders

Complete the concept map on human autosomal genetic disorders. Use these words or phrases one or more times: *Tay-Sachs disease, recessive allele, phenylketonuria, dominant allele, lungs and pancreas, central nervous system, cystic fibrosis.*

Concept Mapping

Chapter
13 Genetic Technology

The Human Genome Project

Complete the concept map on the human genome project. Use these words or phrases one or more times: *chromosomes, frequency of crossovers, distance between genes, polymerase chain reaction, meiosis, the 80 000 genes, DNA fragments of sperm cells, the 46 human chromosomes.*

The Human Genome Project

will map

the 80 000 genes

on

the 46 human chromosomes

techniques used

polymerase chain reaction

makes millions of copies of

DNA fragments of sperm cells

for which scientists analyze the

frequency of crossovers

that occur during

meiosis

frequency of crossovers

helps measure

distance between genes

on

chromosomes

Concept Mapping

Chapter
14 The History of Life

Formation of a Fossil

Make an events chain to show how fossils found in sedimentary rocks are formed, discovered, and dated. **Answers may vary. Possible events chain shown.**

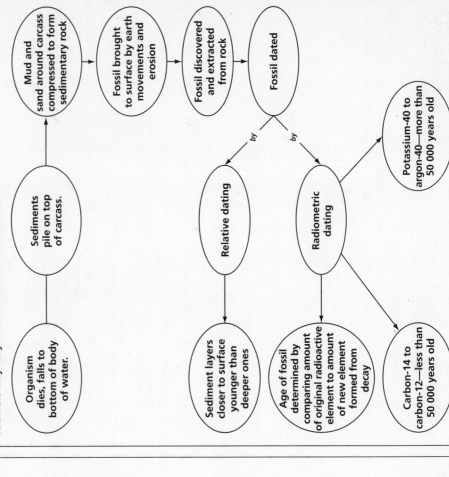

Mud and sand around carcass compressed to form sedimentary rock

Fossil brought to surface by earth movements and erosion

Fossil discovered and extracted from rock

Fossil dated

Sediments pile on top of carcass.

Organism dies, falls to bottom of body of water.

by

Relative dating

by

Radiometric dating

Potassium-40 to argon-40—more than 50 000 years old

Sediment layers closer to surface younger than deeper ones

Age of fossil determined by comparing amount of original radioactive element to amount of new element formed from decay

Carbon-14 to carbon-12—less than 50 000 years old

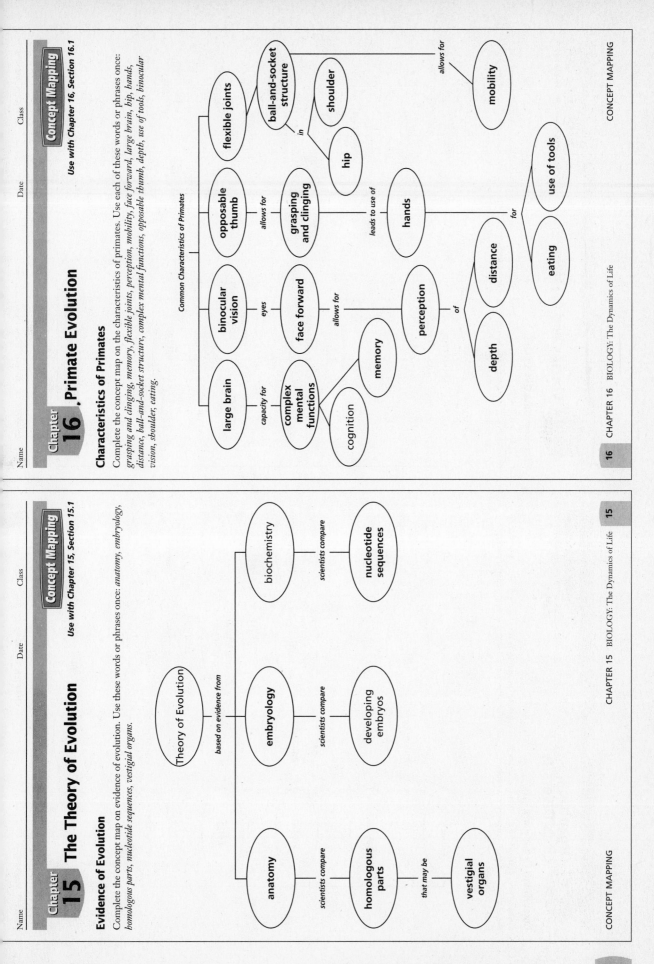

Concept Mapping

Chapter 16 Primate Evolution

Use with Chapter 16, Section 16.1

Characteristics of Primates

Complete the concept map on the characteristics of primates. Use each of these words or phrases once: *grasping and clinging, memory, flexible joints, perception, mobility, face forward, large brain, hip, hands, distance, ball-and-socket structure, complex mental functions, opposable thumb, depth, use of tools, binocular vision, shoulder, eating.*

Common Characteristics of Primates

flexible joints
ball-and-socket structure — allows for → mobility
shoulder
in
hip
opposable thumb — allows for → grasping and clinging — leads to use of → hands — for → use of tools / eating
binocular vision — eyes → face forward — allows for → perception — of → distance / depth
large brain — capacity for → complex mental functions — cognition / memory

---

Concept Mapping

Chapter 15 The Theory of Evolution

Use with Chapter 15, Section 15.1

Evidence of Evolution

Complete the concept map on evidence of evolution. Use these words or phrases once: *anatomy, embryology, homologous parts, nucleotide sequences, vestigial organs.*

Theory of Evolution
based on evidence from
biochemistry — scientists compare → nucleotide sequences
embryology — scientists compare → developing embryos
anatomy — scientists compare → homologous parts — that may be → vestigial organs

Chapter 18 — Viruses and Bacteria

Concept Mapping

Use with Chapter 18, Section 18.1

Viral Reproductive Cycles

Complete the chains of events for the lytic cycle and the lysogenic cycle. Use these words or phrases one or more times: *lytic cycle, host cell, copies viral genes, kills host cell, lysogenic cycle, host cell's chromosome, a provirus, alters, continue, viral DNA, replication of host cell, makes viral protein coat.*

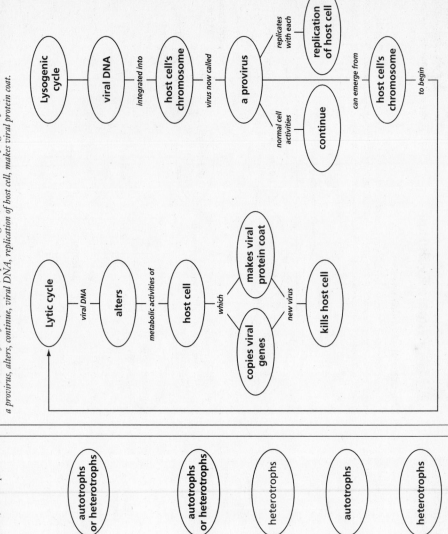

Lysogenic cycle → **viral DNA** — integrated into → **host cell's chromosome** — virus now called → **a provirus**
- replicates with each → **replication of host cell**
- normal cell activities → **continue**
can emerge from → **host cell's chromosome** — to begin →

Lytic cycle — viral DNA → **alters** — metabolic activities of → **host cell** — which →
- **copies viral genes** — new virus → **kills host cell**
- **makes viral protein coat**

Chapter 17 — Organizing Life's Diversity

Concept Mapping

Use with Chapter 17, Sections 17.1, 17.2

Classifying Organisms

Make a concept map identifying the six kingdoms into which organisms are classified. Show whether the organisms in each kingdom are prokaryotes or eukaryotes; unicellular or multicellular; autotrophs or heterotrophs.

Six Kingdoms

- **Eubacteria** → **prokaryotes** → **unicellular** → **autotrophs or heterotrophs**
- **Archaebacteria**
- **Protista** → **eukaryotes** → **unicellular or multicellular** → **autotrophs or heterotrophs**
- **Fungi** → **eukaryotes** → **unicellular or multicellular** → **heterotrophs**
- **Plantae** → **eukaryotes** → **multicellular** → **autotrophs**
- **Animalia** → **eukaryotes** → **multicellular** → **heterotrophs**

Concept Mapping
Use with Chapter 19, Section 19.3

Chapter 19 Protists

Slime Molds

Make a concept map comparing the life cycle of a plasmodial slime mold with that of a cellular slime mold. Use these words or phrases once: meiosis, individual haploid cells that divide by mitosis, haploid during entire life cycle, no meiosis, Acrasiomycota, Myxomycota, cytoplasm with diploid nuclei but no cell walls or membranes, cells become a multicellular mass of amoeboid cells, haploid spores form gametes, engulfs organisms, transforms into many separate spore-producing structures.

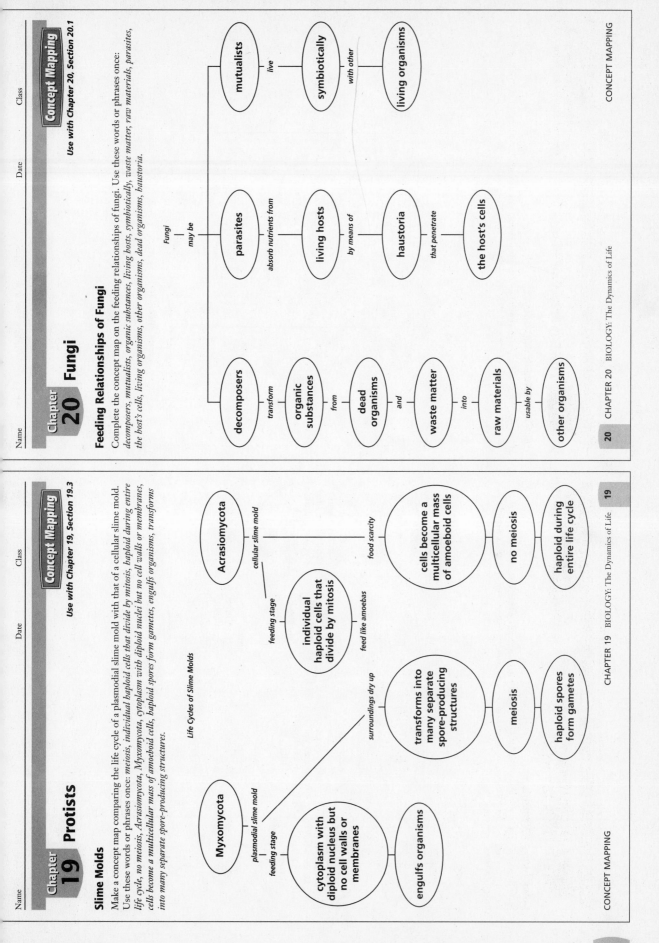

Concept Mapping
Use with Chapter 20, Section 20.1

Chapter 20 Fungi

Feeding Relationships of Fungi

Complete the concept map on the feeding relationships of fungi. Use these words or phrases once: decomposers, mutualists, organic substances, living hosts, symbiotically, waste matter, raw materials, parasites, the host's cells, living organisms, other organisms, dead organisms, haustoria.

Concept Mapping

Chapter 22 The Diversity of Plants

Characteristics of Anthophyta

Complete this concept map comparing the characteristics of the two classes of anthophyta. Use these words or phrases once: *monocotyledons, one seed leaf, two seed leaves, dicotyledons, three, parallel veins, four or five, branched veins*.

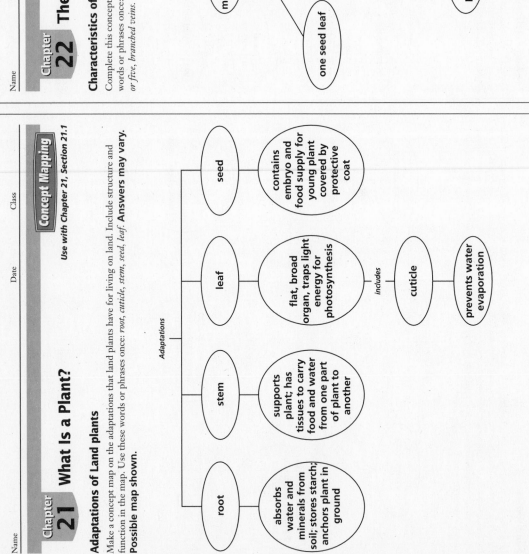

CONCEPT MAPPING

Concept Mapping

Chapter 21 What Is a Plant?

Adaptations of Land plants

Make a concept map on the adaptations that land plants have for living on land. Include structure and function in the map. Use these words or phrases once: *root, cuticle, stem, seed, leaf.* **Answers may vary. Possible map shown.**

Adaptations

- **root** — absorbs water and minerals from soil; stores starch; anchors plant in ground
- **stem** — supports plant; has tissues to carry food and water from one part of plant to another
- **leaf** — flat, broad organ, traps light energy for photosynthesis
  - *includes* **cuticle** — prevents water evaporation
- **seed** — contains embryo and food supply for young plant covered by protective coat

CONCEPT MAPPING

CONCEPT MAPPING

Chapter 23 Plant Structure and Function
Concept Mapping — *Use with Chapter 23, Section 23.1*

Plant Tissues

Complete the concept map of plant tissues. Use these words or phrases once: *apical meristem, cork cambium, dermal, ground, guard cell, lateral meristem, phloem, stomata, vascular, vascular cambium, xylem.* **Answers may vary. Possible map shown.**

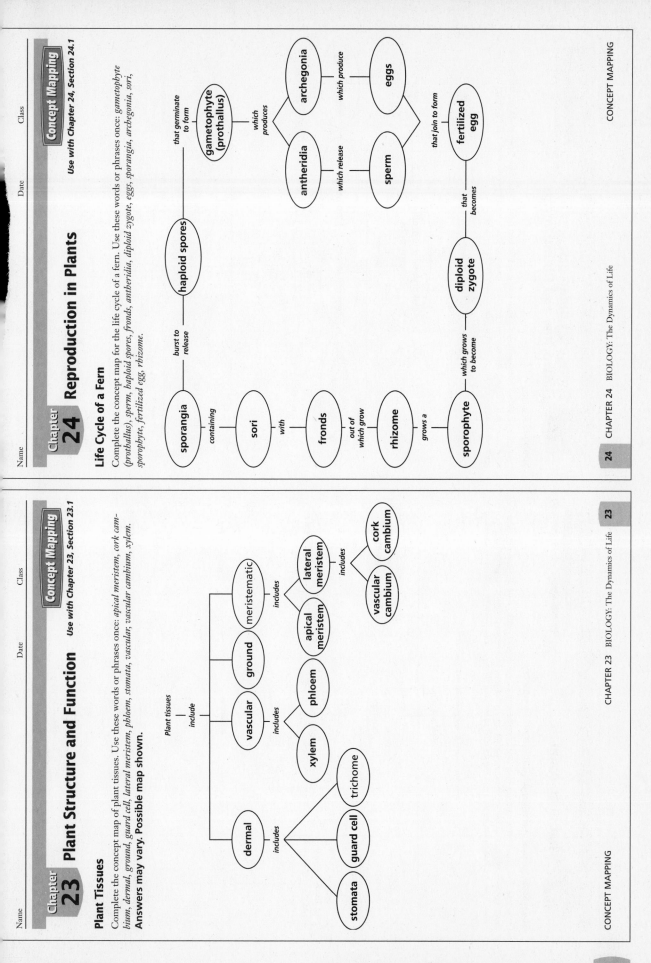

Chapter 24 Reproduction in Plants
Concept Mapping — *Use with Chapter 24, Section 24.1*

Life Cycle of a Fern

Complete the concept map for the life cycle of a fern. Use these words or phrases once: *gametophyte (prothallus), sperm, haploid spores, fronds, antheridia, diploid zygote, eggs, sporangia, archegonia, sori, sporophyte, fertilized egg, rhizome.*

Chapter 25 — What Is an Animal?

Concept Mapping

Use with Chapter 25, Section 25.2

Body Structure of Animals with Bilateral Symmetry

Complete the network tree concept map for the body structure of animals with bilateral symmetry. Use these words or phrases one or more times: *acoelomate animals; no body cavity; support; roundworms; humans, insects, and fishes; mesoderm; complex internal organs; fluid-filled body cavity; coelomate animals; flatworms; muscles.*

Body Structure of Animals with Bilateral Symmetry

Three body plans

- **coelomate animals** — *have* — **fluid-filled body cavity** — *lined with* — **mesoderm** — *that provides space for* — **complex internal organs** — *and include* — **humans, insects, and fishes**

- **pseudocoelomate animals** — *have* — **fluid-filled body cavity** — *lined partially with* — **mesoderm** — *that acts as* — **support** — *for* — **muscles** — *in* — **roundworms**

- **acoelomate animals** — *have* — **no body cavity** — *and include* — **flatworms**

Chapter 26 — Sponges, Cnidarians, Flatworms, and Roundworms

Concept Mapping

Use with Chapter 26, Section 26.1

Sponges

Complete this concept map showing structure and function in a sponge. Use these words or phrases once: *collar cells; no tissues, organs, or organ systems; amoebocytes; pore cells; two cell layers; filter feeding; eukaryotic multicellular heterotrophs; epithelial cells; no body cavity; spicules.*

Sponges

are

- **eukaryotic multicellular heterotrophs** — *that obtain food by* — **filter feeding**
  - *that have*:
    - **no body cavity**
    - **two cell layers** — *made up of* — **four types of cells** — *including*:
      - **pore cells** — *bring water and nutrients into the body*
      - **collar cells** — *have flagella that whip water through the pores*
      - **amoebocytes** — *aid in reproduction* / *carry nutrients to other cells* / *produce chemicals to make* — **spicules**
      - **epithelial cells** — *thin, flat; contract in response to stimuli*
    - **no tissues, organs, or organ systems**

Chapter 27   Mollusks and Segmented Worms

Concept Mapping — Use with Chapter 27, Section 27.2

Segmented Worms

Complete this network tree concept map showing the body organization of the earthworm. Use these words or phrases once : *ventral nerve cord, coelom, brain, excretory organs, bilateral symmetry, crop, reproduction, gizzard, nephridia, anus, nerve fibers, blood, esophagus, segmented body, mouth, blood vessels.*

Chapter 28   Arthropods

Concept Mapping — Use with Chapter 28, Section 28.2

Metamorphosis in Insects

Complete the concept map on metamorphosis in insects. Use these words or phrases one or more times: *complete, internal chemicals, larva, tissue reorganization, adult, four stages, nymph, incomplete, fully developed appendages, reproductive system, egg, grows, three stages, caterpillar, eats leaves, replacement of tissues, molts, pupa.*

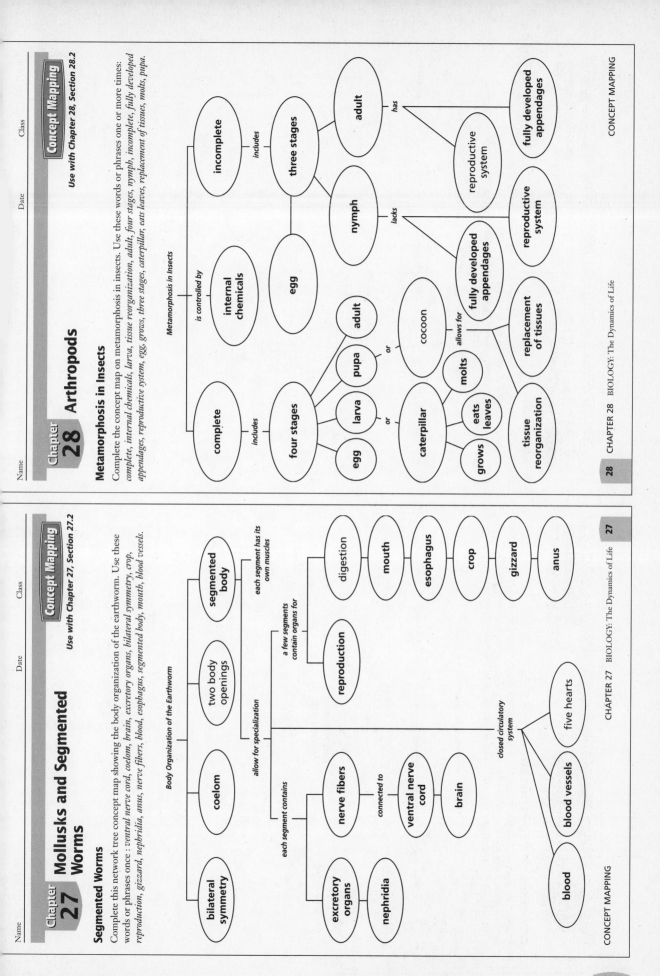

Chapter 29 — Echinoderms and Invertebrate Chordates

Concept Mapping

Use with Chapter 29, Section 29.2

Characteristics of Invertebrate Chordates

Complete the concept map of the characteristics of invertebrate chordates. Use these words or phrases once: *the dorsal hollow nerve cord, posterior portion, the brain, the notochord, each muscle block, the spinal cord, a pair, gill slits, muscle blocks, the tail, the pharynx, nerves, anterior portion.*

Invertebrate Chordates

have

- paired openings — in — the pharynx — called — gill slits
- a hollow tube of cells — called — the dorsal hollow nerve cord
  - provides — a pair — of — nerves — for — each muscle block
  - posterior portion — becomes — the spinal cord
  - anterior portion — becomes — the brain
- semirigid, rodlike structure — called — the notochord — which provides support for — muscle blocks — that move — the tail

---

Chapter 30 — Fishes and Amphibians

Concept Mapping

Use with Chapter 30, Sections 30.1, 30.2

Phylum Chordata

Complete the concept map showing the subphyla and characteristics of the phylum Chordata. Use these words or phrases once: *Urochordata, birds, bilateral symmetry, closed circulatory system, fishes, Cephalochordata, complex brain and sense organs, amphibians, coelomate body plan, Vertebrata, reptiles, efficient respiratory system.*

Subphyla of the Phylum Chordata

- Urochordata
- Vertebrata — Classes include — fishes, amphibians, reptiles, birds, mammals
- Cephalochordata

Characteristics
- bilateral symmetry
- coelomate body plan
- efficient respiratory system
- closed circulatory system
- complex brain and sense organs

Chapter 31 Reptiles and Birds

Adaptations for Flight

Complete the concept map of the adaptations that allow birds to fly. Use these words or phrases once: *powerful muscles, wings, hollow bones, inhaling, ability to maintain high energy level, lightweight body, air sacs, sternum, digestive system that can handle large amounts of food, exhaling, beak made of keratin, feathers, no teeth or jaw, lungs, oxygenated air.*

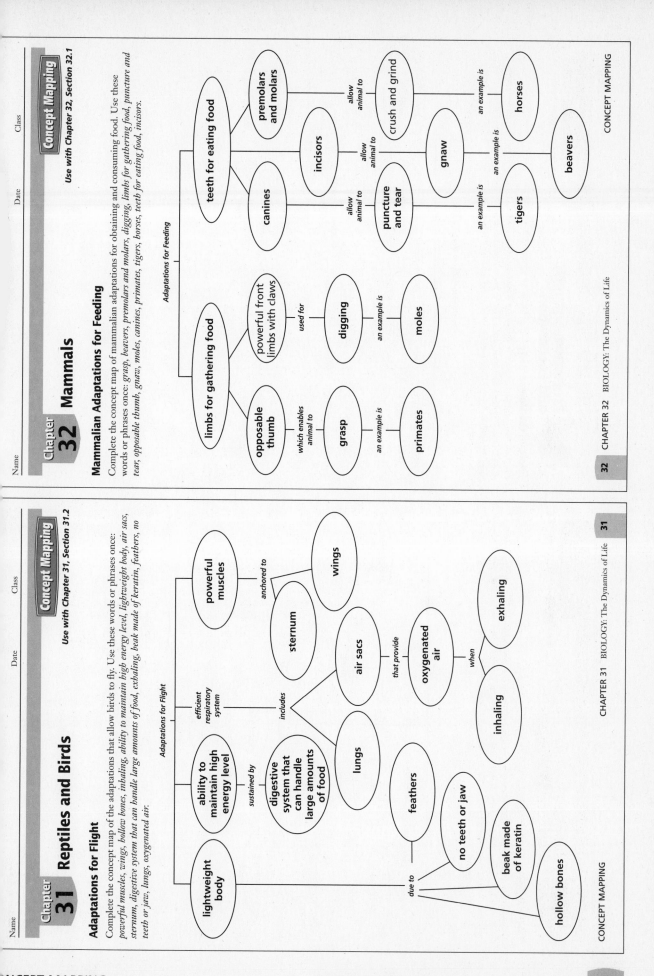

Chapter 32 Mammals

Mammalian Adaptations for Feeding

Complete the concept map of mammalian adaptations for obtaining and consuming food. Use these words or phrases once: *grasp, beavers, premolars and molars, digging, limbs for gathering food, puncture and tear, opposable thumb, gnaw, moles, canines, primates, tigers, horses, teeth for eating food, incisors.*

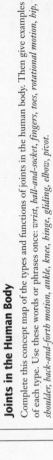

Chapter 34 Protection, Support, and Locomotion

Joints in the Human Body

Complete this concept map of the types and functions of joints in the human body. Then give examples of each type. Use these words or phrases once: *wrist, ball-and-socket, fingers, toes, rotational motion, hip, shoulder, back-and-forth motion, ankle, knee, hinge, gliding, elbow, pivot.*

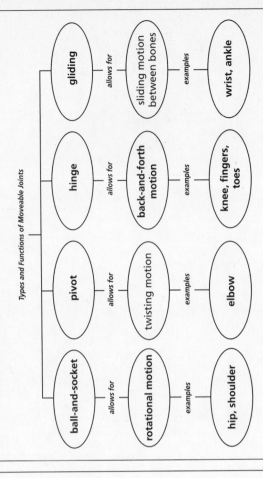

Types and Functions of Moveable Joints

ball-and-socket — pivot — hinge — gliding

ball-and-socket *allows for* rotational motion *examples* hip, shoulder

pivot *allows for* twisting motion *example* elbow

hinge *allows for* back-and-forth motion *examples* knee, fingers, toes

gliding *allows for* sliding motion between bones *examples* wrist, ankle

---

Chapter 33 Animal Behavior

Territoriality

Complete the concept map of the role played by territoriality in the survival of species. Use these words or phrases once: *dominance hierarchy, population growth, survival, injury to either male, other animals, aggressive behavior, species as a whole, limited resources, dominance, submission of the weaker male, young, pheromones, territories.*

Territoriality —

improves chance of survival *for* young, species as a whole

establishes territories *marked by* pheromones

reduces competition for limited resources

controls population growth

establishes dominance *by means of* aggressive behavior

aggressive behavior *which intimidates* other animals

aggressive behavior *which is followed by* submission of the weaker male *which leads to a* dominance hierarchy

aggressive behavior *which prevents* injury to either male

Chapter 36 — The Nervous System

Concept Mapping Use with Chapter 36, Section 36.2

The Sense of Touch

Complete this concept map for the sense of touch. Use these words or phrases one or more times: *dermis, temperature, nerve endings, heat, cold, light pressure, eyelids, skin surface, tip of tongue, palms of hands, epidermis, fingertips, organs, muscle tissue, lower layers, heavy pressure, soles of feet.*

Chapter 35 — The Digestive and Endocrine Systems

Concept Mapping Use with Chapter 35, Section 35.2

Carbohydrates, Fats, and Proteins in Nutrition

Complete this concept map showing the role of carbohydrates, fats, and proteins in nutrition. Use these words or phrases once: *muscles, antibodies, carbohydrates, proteins, chemicals for blood-clotting, amino acids, glycerol, body functions, fatty acids, the liver, indigestible cellulose, glycogen, fat, body cells, hormones, cell structure, enzymes, simple sugars.*

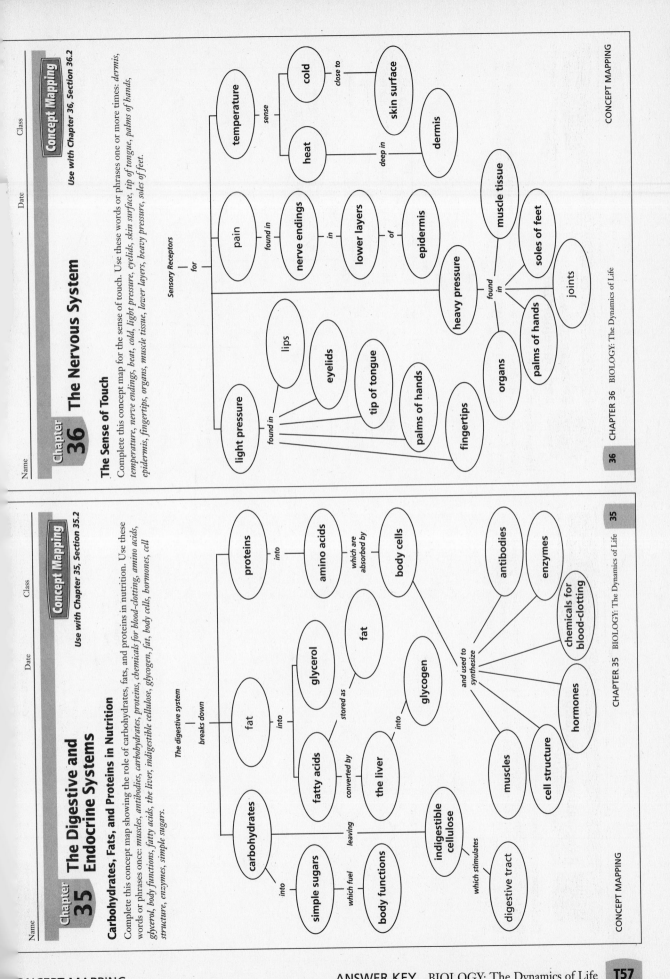

Chapter 38 Reproduction and Development

Concept Mapping

Use with Chapter 38, Section 38.1

Human Growth

Make a concept map showing the different stages of human growth and their characteristics. Use these words or phrases once: *puberty, human growth, two years, embryo, zygote, fetus, slower metabolism, teen years, physical and intellectual activity.*

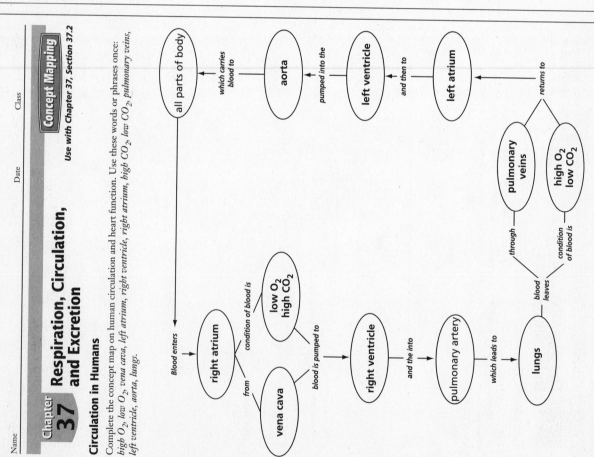

Concept map (Chapter 38) nodes and connectors:

- **Human growth** — can be divided into five stages
  - development before birth — during which a fertilized egg becomes a **zygote** — then a — blastocyst — Once in the uterus the — **embryo** — continues to develop into a — **fetus** — until birth
  - infancy — which lasts from — birth — through — **two years**
  - childhood — spans from 2 years to — **puberty** — Which is characterized by — steady growth — and the development of the — ability to reason — and to solve problems
  - adolescence — includes the — **teen years** — during which the adolescent reaches — maximum physical stature; slower metabolism
  - adulthood — characterized by — **physical and intellectual activity** — the ability to maintain

CONCEPT MAPPING

Chapter 37 Respiration, Circulation, and Excretion

Concept Mapping

Use with Chapter 37, Section 37.2

Circulation in Humans

Complete the concept map on human circulation and heart function. Use these words or phrases once: $high\ O_2\ low\ O_2$, vena cava, left atrium, right ventricle, right atrium, $high\ CO_2\ low\ CO_2$, pulmonary veins, left ventricle, aorta, lungs.

Concept map (Chapter 37) nodes and connectors:

- Blood enters → **right atrium** — condition of blood is — **low O_2 high CO_2**; from — **vena cava** — blood is pumped to — **right ventricle** — and the into — pulmonary artery — which leads to — **lungs** — blood leaves — through — **pulmonary veins**; condition of blood is — **high O_2 low CO_2** — returns to — **left atrium** — and then to — **left ventricle** — pumped into the — **aorta** — which carries blood to — all parts of body

CONCEPT MAPPING

CONCEPT MAPPIN

Name _____   Date _____   Class _____

Chapter 39 Immunity from Disease

Concept Mapping

Use with Chapter 39, Section 39.2

The Lymphatic System

Complete the concept map about the structure of the lymphatic system and how it defends the body against disease. Use these words or phrases one or more times: *foreign substances, two ducts, tissue fluid, lymph, white blood cells, lymph veins, protect body, nodes, bloodstream, lymphocytes, lymph capillaries.*

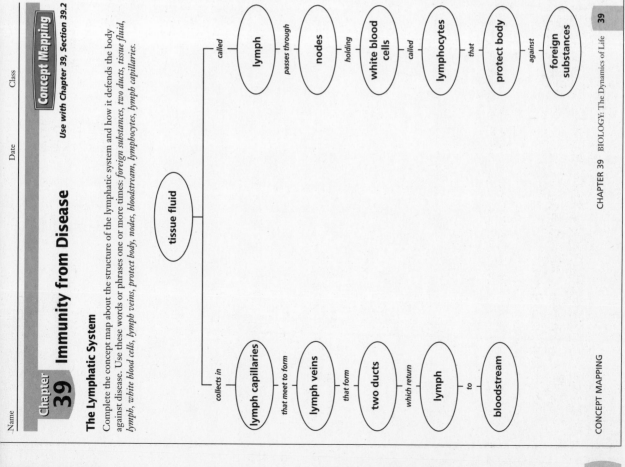

CONCEPT MAPPING

CHAPTER 39   BIOLOGY: The Dynamics of Life   **39**

CONCEPT MAPPING

ANSWER KEY   BIOLOGY: The Dynamics of Life   **T59**